HANDBOOK

Understanding and Controlling
Electromagnetic Fields in Your Life

Stephen Prata

Waite Group Press™
Corte Madera, CA

Publisher • *Mitchell Waite*
Editorial Director • *Scott Calamar*
Managing Editor • *Joel Fugazzotto*
Content Editor • *Heidi Brumbaugh*
Technical Reviewer • *Mary Burns*
Production Director • *Julianne Ososke*
Cover Design • *Ted Mader*
Design • *Ted Mader, Sestina Quarequio*
Production • *Sestina Quarequio*
Illustration • *Ben Long*

© 1993 by The Waite Group, Inc.®
Published by Waite Group Press™, 200 Tamal Plaza, Corte Madera, CA 94925

Waite Group Press™ is distributed to bookstores and book wholesalers by Publishers Group West, Box 8843, Emeryville, CA 94662, 1-800-788-3123 (in California 1-510-658-3453).

Printed in the United States of America
93 94 95 96 • 10 9 8 7 6 5 4 3 2 1

Library of Congress Cataloging-in-Publication Data
Prata, Stephen
        EMF handbook: understanding and controlling electromagnetic fields in your life
/ Stephen Prata.
            p.   cm.
        Includes index.
        ISBN 1-878739-55-7 : $12.95 ($16.95 Can,)
    1. Electromagnetic fields--Health aspects. 2. Electromagnetic fields--Safety measures. I. Title.
QP82.2.E43P73 1993
612'.01442--dc20   93-25399
                                                                                        CIP

Dedication

I dedicate this book to my sweetheart and wife, Kathleen.

Acknowledgments

I wish to thank Mitchell Waite for suggesting and planning this book, and Joel Fugazzotto and Scott Calamar for gathering materials and guiding the book to completion. I particularly wish to thank Heidi Brumbaugh for her perceptive and intelligent editorial advice.

About the Author

Stephen Prata teaches astronomy, physics, and computer science at the College of Marin in Kentfield, California. He received his B.S. from the California Institute of Technology and his Ph.D. from the University of California, Berkeley. Stephen has authored or coauthored over a dozen books for The Waite Group, including *UNIX Primer Plus, Microsoft Quick C Programming, Microsoft Quick Basic Primer Plus,* and *Artificial Life Playhouse.* He also wrote *The Waite Group's New C Primer Plus,* which received the Computer Press Association's 1990 Best How-to Computer Book Award and *The Waite Group's C++ Primer Plus,* nominated for the Computer Press Association's Best How-to Computer Book Award in 1991.

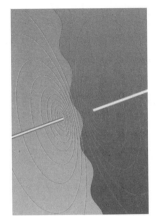

Introduction

"ELECTROMAGNETIC FUROR"...
"CONTROLLING EMFs"... "ELUSIVE
EMF THREAT"... Articles and TV news
reports with titles like these appear with
increasing frequency as the press reflects
community concerns about EMFs, a form of energy that
emanates invisibly from electrical equipment and power
lines. If you've read one of these articles or caught a news
story on the subject, you may have gathered that there is a
connection between EMFs and certain forms of disease.
You may be concerned about your children playing under
electric power lines, a clock radio too close to your bed, or a
house that might be "sick".

The Waite Group asked me to write this book because
my background is in physical science education, including
teaching physics for non-science students. We agreed that a
handbook about EMFs would be a valuable project, one
that could help concerned readers to educate themselves on
the facts and issues involved.

This book provides you with the background you need
to understand one of today's most controversial technological issues: the possible dangers of EMFs. *EMF Handbook*
reviews what we know about EMFs and outlines what you
can do about the risks.

The first three chapters are a simple exploration of
EMFs which tells how to reduce the occurrence of these
electric fields in our daily life. The remaining three chapters
provide a more in-depth presentation of the risk, detailing
important EMF research and revealing the physics behind
EMFs in a user friendly fashion.

You'll find a visual and easy-to-understand approach which includes hands-on experiments, information boxes, and technical explanations that are organized for technical and non-technical readers alike.

We hope you find this book helpful in both understanding EMFs and reducing their daily occurrence.

Stephen Prata

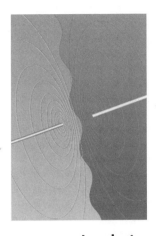

Table of Contents

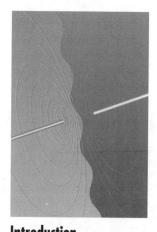

Contents

EMFs and You

You've probably seen or heard stories recently that describe a potential threat to our health, and particularly to the health of our children: electromagnetic fields or EMFs. Some stories have discussed how nearby electric power lines placed school children in danger. Others have described concerns in the workplace about radiation from computer terminals, and concerns in the home about EMFs from the electrical wiring. You have probably gathered the following:

⤷ EMFs have something to do with electricity and electrical power lines.

⤷ EMFs are said to be linked to increased cancer risks.

To introduce you to this important topic, this chapter answers some of the most common questions about EMFs. You'll find more detail in the following chapters.

Questions and Answers

What are EMFs, and where do they come from?

EMF stands for *electromagnetic field*. Electromagnetic fields are one of the most common components of the natural universe. For instance, light, radio waves, and microwaves are made of electromagnetic fields. The term EMF refers to a particular variety of electromagnetic fields, those produced by the electric currents in our power lines, household wiring, and appliances. Figure 1-1 illustrates some of the usual suspects.

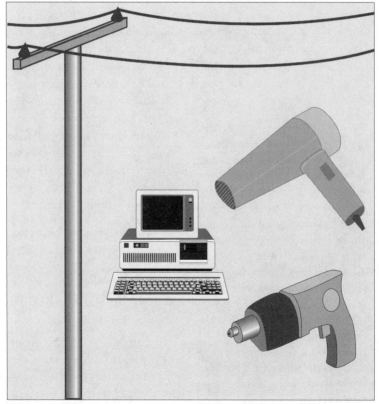

Figure 1-1 EMF sources

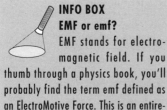

INFO BOX
EMF or emf?
EMF stands for electromagnetic field. If you thumb through a physics book, you'll probably find the term emf defined as an ElectroMotive Force. This is an entirely different emf from the EMF we'll be talking about. Remember, careless thumbing through a physics book can be hazardous to your understanding.

Is there another name for EMFs?

Yes. They are called *power frequency fields* because they come from the electric power system. They are called 60-Hz fields because they oscillate in strength 60 times a second. Hz is short for *Hertz*, which is the scientific unit for measuring oscillations or vibrations per second. (Much of the world uses 50-Hz power instead of 60-Hz power, but this book will just use 60-Hz for simplicity.)

EMFs are also called ELF radiation. ELF stands for *extra-low frequency* because 60 Hz is an extremely low oscillation rate compared to most other electromagnetic fields, such as those associated with radio waves and light. Technically ELF is a more precise term than EMF. On the other hand, headlines like "ELF CONTROVERSY" might lead the reader to think the article had something to do with labor practices in Santa's workshop.

Haven't I heard the term Hz somewhere before?

AM radio station settings are described in kiloHertz (kHz), and FM radio settings are described in megaHertz (MHz). A kHz is 1,000 Hertz, and an MHz is 1 million Hertz. For example, an AM dial setting of 740 means 740 kHz, or 740,000 Hz, and an FM dial setting of 102.1 MHz means a frequency of 102.1 million Hertz. These values represent the number of oscillations per second in the electromagnetic fields broadcast by the stations. As you can see, EMFs of 50 Hz or 60 Hz really have extra-low frequencies compared to radio.

Why do people think EMFs are harmful?

Recent *epidemiological* research (statistical case studies) in the United States and in Sweden show an increased incidence of childhood leukemia among children raised in homes with higher levels of EMFs. Although other similar studies have failed to support this finding, the studies that do find a connection include the three largest and most carefully executed research projects.

Are EMFs a harmful form of radiation that, like X-rays or radioactivity, can directly harm living tissue?

The frequencies of radiation associated with 60-Hz AC currents have far too little energy to damage the molecules in a cell. The direct effect is comparable to the damage an ant would inflict on an armored tank by crashing into it. The effects of EMFs, if any, would be more in the nature of a subtle influence, analogous to the ant crawling into the tank's electronic control system and causing a short circuit.

Do laboratory studies back up the statistical case studies?

The laboratory results are mixed. Twenty years ago most scientists thought it unlikely that EMFs could have *any* biological effects whatsoever. Since then research has demonstrated that EMFs can have biological effects. As far as harmful effects go, several experiments have failed to show any link between cancer and EMFs, while others suggest (but don't prove) that a link does exist.

What sort of EMF–cancer links do laboratory studies suggest?

1. Rather than causing cancer, EMFs may promote the development of existing cancers. In other words the presence of EMFs may cause a cancer to progress that might otherwise have been suppressed by the immune system.

2. EMFs may suppress production of the hormone melatonin, which, in turn may weaken the body's immune system response to cancer.

These results don't prove that EMFs cause or promote cancer. They do begin to make it plausible that such connections could exist, and they point the way to further research.

Is there a consensus as to what all the conflicting evidence about EMFs means?

Some researchers are convinced that EMFs are dangerous; others are convinced they are harmless. From the scientific standpoint, this means we need more research. Insofar as there is a consensus, it is that EMFs are a *possible* health danger.

Does the U.S. government have anything to say on the subject?

Two U.S. government agencies analyzed recent research and came up with similar conclusions. The Office of Technology Assessment (OTA) issued a 1989 report that stated, "The emerging evidence no longer allows one to categorically assert that there are no risks." (Appendix A contains more detailed references for this and other technical articles mentioned in this book.) A 1990 report from the Environmental Protection Agency (EPA) concludes, "With our current understanding, we can identify 60-Hz magnetic fields from power lines and perhaps other sources in the home as a possible, but not proven, cause of cancer in humans." Most likely it will take years of additional research to establish a definitive answer. Meanwhile the reports suggest that it is reasonable to take "prudent" measures to reduce possible risks.

What are prudent measures?

Prudent measures are low-cost or no-cost actions to reduce exposures to EMFs. The next two chapters and the end of this chapter discuss examples.

How can I determine my exposure to EMFs?

Many power companies will survey your home for EMFs for free, or

INFO BOX
Names
The unit used most commonly in measuring magnetic fields is called the gauss (rhymes with house), named after German mathematician, astronomer, and physicist Karl Friedrich Gauss, whose face graces the ten-Deutschmark bill. The magnetic fields associated with EMFs are relatively small, and they usually are measured in milligauss, with one milligauss (mG) being one-thousandth of a gauss (G). For comparison the Earth's magnetic field (the one that makes compasses point north) has a strength of about 500 mG, or one-half gauss. Don't confuse the milligauss (mG) with the milligram (mg).

for a small fee. In some localities you can hire a private service to survey your home. You can also buy, or perhaps rent, an EMF meter and make your own readings.

What does an EMF meter measure?

It measures the magnetic component of the electromagnetic field. That's because the magnetic part penetrates the human body, while the electric part doesn't. So any EMF effects on a living organism would come from the magnetic part.

Is it true that the magnetic fields associated with EMFs are so small compared to the Earth's magnetic field that they couldn't have any biological effect?

It's true that electromagnetic fields typically are much weaker than the Earth's magnetic field. But EMFs oscillate, which means they can generate small electric currents in living tissue. In principle these currents could mimic or interfere with natural electrical activity in a cell. Some laboratory experiments do seem to show real bioeffects stemming from EMFs. The Earth's magnetic field, on the other hand, is steady, or *static,* not oscillating, and a static magnetic field does not generate small electric currents.

What's an unsafe level of EMFs?

We don't know. We don't even know if the strength of the field is the most important factor in determining biological effects. One idea being studied further is that variations in the field strength are more important than the strength itself. That is, moving in and out of a strong field may have more effect than simply sitting in a strong field. A second promising idea is that certain combinations of the geomagnetic field and EMF fields resonate together, increasing effects.

Don't recent studies prove that 2.5 mG EMFs cause cancer in children?

There are a couple of misconceptions here. Epidemiological studies (statistical studies) have indicated that being exposed to fields of 2.5 mG and above increases the risk of childhood leukemia by about a factor of two.

The first misconception has to do with the 2.5-mG level. This level originally was chosen arbitrarily to divide households into high- and low-exposure groups. It could turn out that the low end of the high-exposure group really isn't at much risk, or it could turn out that the high end of the low-exposure group is at some risk. The truth is that we don't know what a safe level is. We don't yet know if the field strength is the only or even the most important factor in determining risk.

The second misconception is that studies have *proven* that EMFs cause cancer. First, the number of cases considered in each study is too low to permit a convincing statistical conclusion. As Dr. John Peters reported in his Los Angeles study, their data offered "little support for the relationship between measured magnetic field exposure and leukemia risk, some support for a relationship between wiring configuration and leukemia risk." Note that "little support" means weak support, which is stronger than no support. Even the largest study (Ahlbom and Feychting, 1992) has been criticized for having too small a sample size. On the other hand, although each study is weak statistically, the fact that they all had more or less the same results argues that there is a real effect.

However, even if we accept the studies at face value, they don't show that EMFs *cause* cancer. Instead they show that EMFs *increase the risk* of cancer. That is, exposing the whole country to EMFs doesn't mean that everyone will get leukemia, it just means that everyone is more likely to get it. Instead of 40 out every 1 million children contracting child leukemia, 80 out of 1 million would. This would be tragic for the extra 40 children per million that get the disease, but the vast majority would be unaffected.

Isn't it true that there is no scientific evidence supporting the claim that EMFs cause cancer?

This is true but misleading. Epidemiological studies, by their very nature, show statistical connections, not cause-and-effect. Current statistical studies suggest that there is a weak connection between EMFs and cancer.

Laboratory experiments, on the other hand, *do* have the potential to unearth cause-and-effect relationships. To date no experiment has demonstrated that EMFs cause cancer. However, several experiments do show that EMFs can have biological effects and suggest (but not prove) that EMFs may promote an existing cancer.

If 2.5 mG is bad for you, then wouldn't 25 mG be a lot worse?

The idea here is that the adverse effects of EMFs are proportional to the strength of the field. This is called a dose-response relationship. An example of a *dose-response* relationship is the observation that heavy smokers are more likely to get lung cancer than moderate smokers, while moderate smokers are more likely to get lung cancer than nonsmokers. The evidence for this sort of relationship between EMFs and health effects is inconclusive. A few studies have found such a relationship; most studies haven't; and other studies suggest that factors other than field strength are important.

Aren't high-voltage electrical transmission lines the chief cause of EMFs?

EMF radiation weakens very rapidly with distance, so high-voltage lines are an important EMF source only to locations within a few hundred feet of power lines. For most people the following sources are more important: electrical appliances, home wiring (particularly if some of the wiring has been done incorrectly or if there is multiple grounding), and the local distribution lines. Many objectionable aspects of high-voltage lines, such as high-pitched hums, crackling noises, and the like have nothing to do with EMF magnetic fields.

Many parents and teachers are concerned about the proximity of high-voltage power lines to their schools. In many

> **DO IT**
> **The Influence of the Pencil Sharpener**
> The motor in an electric pencil sharpener can produce magnetic fields of 1,000 mG. These fields weaken rapidly with distance, but they still are strong enough to distort a video display, as shown in Figure 1-2. The display is "painted" by a beam of electrons that scans back and forth over the screen. The magnetic fields produced by the pencil sharpener deflect the beam, producing the distortions you see. Naturally the distortions are greatest closest to the pencil sharpener.

Figure 1-2 Pencil sharpener emanations distort a video display

situations, exposures to EMFs can be reduced by changing the power-line wiring system, as discussed in Chapter 3, or by elevating the wires to increase the distance. For example, Pacific Gas and Electric recently reducing magnetic field levels by 50 to 75% in a Mill Valley, California school by raising the power lines an additional 20 feet.

Won't putting power lines underground get rid of EMFs?

This has a no-yes-no kind of answer. The first no is because the earth does not provide any shielding of 60-Hz magnetic fields, so simply putting the lines underground doesn't help.

The yes comes from the fact that packing the lines more closely increases a cancellation effect in which fields from one line partially cancel fields from another line. Because underground lines use oil instead of air to insulate the lines, underground lines can be packed together more closely, thus increasing the cancellation effect and reducing EMFs.

The second no comes from the fact that cancellation is effective only for balanced currents. If some of the return current travels through the ground or along metal water pipes, instead of through the power lines, then part of the current in the power lines will be unbalanced. An unbalanced current of, say, 10 amps produces the same magnetic field whether the wires are underground or strung on poles. But the underground wires would be closer to us and our homes, thus exposing us to more EMFs. Chapter 3 discusses the cancellation effect in more detail.

In short: underground lines will reduce (but not get rid of) EMFs, providing the grounding problems that produce stray return currents are kept under control. Similar effects can be achieved at less cost by modifying or redesigning power line poles. Power companies seem to suspect some groups of raising the EMF issue in order to add emotional clout to their real objective, which is putting power lines underground for aesthetic reasons.

Why can't scientists give a simple yes-or-no answer to the question of whether EMFs cause cancer?

The reason is that there is no obvious physical cause-and-effect relationship. Exposure to EMFs doesn't do something obvious, such as turning your ears green or liquefying your skeleton. So scientists either have to look for indirect evidence or probe for hidden relationships. To date research has presented a mixed bag, with some studies finding that EMFs may have harmful effects and other studies failing to find any connection. We need more research to understand what's going on.

What's this about more research?

From the scientific standpoint, we need more research into fundamental mechanisms. A living cell is an exceedingly complex structure from the electrochemical viewpoint, so there are many avenues to investigate. However, funding for this area of research is relatively small and much of the available funding comes from the power industry though 6.5 million dollars in Federal funds was passed in 1992 by the National Energy Policy Department. You can look at this either as evidence of the power industry's commitment to unraveling the mystery of EMFs, or as a recipe for conflict of interest. Probably there are elements of truth in both views.

What can we expect from more research?

A better understanding of what's going on could pin-point the exact risks of EMFs and suggest effective ways to minimize them. If EMFs do prove to be a health hazard, the best solution may turn out to be something completely different from currently proposed solutions. Or the current evidence that EMFs are a risk could turn out to be anomalies that will disappear with more extensive investigation. The disappearance of unusual effects with the maturation of an investigation is a common occurrence in science. However, this scenario seem less likely than it did a few years ago.

What if I don't want to wait years and years for a definitive understanding to evolve?

From the standpoint of public health policy, the situation is unsatisfactory. Waiting years for definitive scientific results can cost needless deaths if it turns out that EMFs are a significant health hazard. Making large-scale changes such as modifying our system for distributing electrical power would be extremely expensive and would be wasteful if it turned out that EMFs are not a significant health hazard or that there were other less expensive but more effective measures possible. This brings us back to prudent avoidance. This policy is based on the fact that much of our exposures to EMFs comes from wiring and appliances in the home, not from external power lines. The strongest connection that one study found was that between child leukemia and exposure to electric hair dryers and black-and-white televisions. You can reduce those exposures with only modest outlays of time, money, and effort.

What can I do?

To follow a course of prudent avoidance, you first have to identify those locations in your home, school, or workplace that have high levels of EMFs. You can do any or all of the following:

◆ In many places, you can ask your local utility company to check out your home, school, or workplace for free.

↳ You can hire an EMF consultant to do the checking.

↳ You can borrow, rent, or buy an EMF meter and do your own checking. Chapter 2 provides guidance on making your own measurements.

Here is a checklist of prudent actions adapted from an article in the March 8, 1993 issue of the *San Francisco Chronicle:*

↳ Move your bed if it is located near where the electrical power line enters the house.

↳ Avoid using electric blankets. (Some newer models use a wiring scheme that greatly reduces EMFs.)

↳ Insist that your children sit at least five feet from the TV screen.

↳ Keep electric alarm clocks at least three feet from your sleeping position.

↳ Consider not using your electric razor and handheld hair dryer.

↳ Don't stand beside your microwave oven or dishwasher when they are operating.

↳ Adjust your desk and sitting position so that your head remains some distance away from a fluorescent or halogen lamp.

↳ Stay an arm's length away from your computer screen and three feet from nearby terminals. (Computer monitors emit more EMF radiation to the sides and to the rear than they do straight ahead.)

↳ If your home has "tube and knob" wiring (see Chapter 3), you may wish to replace it with modern wiring.

Of course, prudent avoidance doesn't help much with EMFs generated by the power lines. Here EMF reduction becomes a matter of public rather than private policy. If you are convinced that a nearby transformer is a threat to your family's health, you either have to move (which has the ethically dubious consequence of putting the next occupant at risk), or you have to convince your power company to do something about it.

What Else Is in This Book?

This chapter poses and answers many interesting questions. The rest of the book deals with these same topics, plus additional topics, in greater detail.

Chapter 2 outlines how an EMF meter works and how you can use one to survey your home for EMFs.

Chapter 3 looks at various EMF sources (electrical appliances, your home's wiring system, and electric power lines) and discusses what you can do to minimize your exposure to EMFs.

The apparent danger of EMFs is not that they are guaranteed to cause cancer, but that they increase the odds of contracting cancer. Chapter 4 discusses how risk is evaluated, how to assess the importance of a risk, and some of the factors that go into the perception of risk.

Chapter 5 examines what research tells us about the effects of EMFs. It looks into residential studies, occupational studies, and laboratory experiments.

Chapter 6 outlines the physics behind EMFs, explaining related concepts such as electricity, magnetism, fields, and currents.

Appendix A presents further reading you may wish to pursue. Appendix B is a glossary. It provides short definitions for the various technical terms that appear in this book. Appendix C is a table of typical EMF levels produced by various household electrical devices.

Measuring EMFs

If you are worried about EMFs, the first step is to locate where they are. Many public utilities will check your home for free or for a small fee. You may find a private company in your area that will examine your home, or you can get an EMF meter and measure the fields yourself. The do-it-yourself approach has a couple of advantages:

⤵ In some parts of the country, you may not have the option of having a public utility or other company do the job.

⤵ EMF levels vary during the day and night, and by doing it yourself, you can monitor the field strength at any time.

QUICK LOOK
To evaluate EMF exposures at your home, workplace, or school, have a public utility or private company scan the area with an EMF meter, or obtain a meter and scan the area yourself. The usual EMF sources are power lines, your home's wiring system, and electric appliances. Usually the in-house sources are the most important. This chapter outlines a systematic approach to surveying the fields.

There also are some disadvantages:

⤵ Meters can be expensive.

⤵ You have to know how to use the meter and where to look for EMFs.

This chapter will brief you on how to use a meter and where to measure. Even if you have someone else make an EMF survey, reading this chapter will help you understand what's going on. The next chapter will look into what actions you can take if you find high EMF levels.

One important question about field strengths is, what is a safe level? The answer, unfortunately, is that we don't know. Many people have settled on 2.5 mG as a significant level, but the choice of that value is partially accidental. An early study comparing high and low exposures to EMFs arbitrarily chose 2.5 mG as the dividing line between the two groups. Ultimately research may arrive at some other level as "safe."

Other factors may be involved. For instance, a smaller field that varies a lot in strength may turn out to be more hazardous than a larger field that is more stable. Or risk may depend on the interaction between the EMFs and the local geomagnetic field, something that doesn't show up in simple meter readings. Or there may be no real health hazard. But for now the judicious thing to do is to identify where the fields are strongest and then take appropriate action.

The Meter

EMF meters range in price from about $90 to $10,000. The less expensive meters tend to measure a narrow range of magnetic field frequencies, for example, just 50 Hz or 60 Hz or perhaps 30 Hz to 300. More expensive ones may reach frequencies up to 50 kHz or more.

Meters differ in their sensitivities. One might measure fields in the range of 1 mG to 2,000 mG, another might measure 0.1 mG to 100 mG, and so on. The meter might be called a gauss meter, an EMF meter, an ELF meter, an electromagnetic meter, a magnetic

IN DEPTH
Meter Scales
We've been assuming that your EMF meter measures in milligauss (mG, for short). However, some measure fields in microteslas (μT). There are 10,000 gauss to a tesla, which means that there are 10 mG per (μT).

To convert μT to mG:
multiply the μT value by 10

For example, 0.2 μT are 2 mG. Another unit you may encounter is the nanotesla (nT).

To convert a nanotesla to milligauss:
divide the nT value by 100

For example, 200 nT are 2 mG. Scientists and engineers use the prefix milli to indicate one-thousandth, the prefix micro to indicate one-millionth, and the prefix nano to indicate one one-thousand-millionth, or one-billionth, in American terminology.

scanner, a magnetic flux meter, or something else. To monitor EMFs you'd want a meter capable of reading fields as low as 1 mG. An electronics store is a good place to look for EMF meters.

INSIDE A METER

Here's how the EMF meter works. First, you need to know that a changing magnetic field produces a changing electric field. The EMF meter detects changing fields with a wire coil. If the changing magnetic field is aligned with the axis of the coil, the changing electric field produces an AC voltage in the coil, which the meter can measure (see Figure 2-1). The bigger the change in the magnetic field, the bigger the voltage, so the meter can use the voltage to calculate the strength of the magnetic field. (For more on changing magnetic fields, see Chapter 6.)

Notice that the meter design picks up changing magnetic fields, like those associated with EMFs. It doesn't pick up the geomagnetic field because that field isn't oscillating.

The loop sensor is directional. It responds most strongly if the changing magnetic field is parallel to the axis of the loop. Most meters are *single-axis* meters, meaning that they have a single coil. When using a single-axis meter, you should turn the meter in various directions until you get the strongest reading. That means you've aligned the coil with the field and are getting a true reading. Figure 2-2 shows a single-axis meter. The double-ended arrow marked ELF SENSOR indicates the location and direction of the sensing coil.

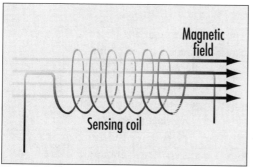

Figure 2-1 The sensing coil

Some meters are *three-axis* meters, meaning they have three coils oriented at right angles to each other. A three-axis meter combines measurements from all three coils to measure the magnetic field. That means you don't have to turn the meter in various directions; it should give the same reading no matter how it is oriented.

USING A METER

For the details on using a meter, you'll have to consult the meter's manual. The simplest ones you just turn on and off. Others may require that you set a range for the field strength and possibly frequency.

When taking measurements, keep in mind the following three points:

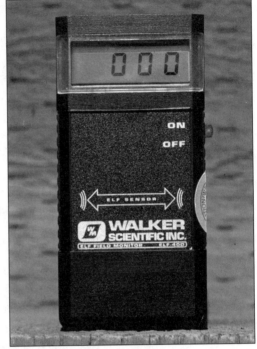

Figure 2-2 A single-axis EMF meter

⮥ Magnetic fields are directional.

⮥ The meter should be stationary when you take your readings.

⮥ Magnetic field strengths weaken very rapidly with distance from the source.

The first point is critical if you are using a single-axis meter. It means you have to experiment when using the meter, turning it in various directions until you get the maximum reading.

The second point stems from the fact that the very act of rotating a meter can generate spurious readings as the movement changes the alignment between the magnetic field and the sensor coil. For instance, twisting the meter suddenly in a field of 180 mG may generate a temporary reading of 600 mG. So only use readings obtained from a stationary meter.

The magnetic field strength depends dramatically upon distance from the source. For example, magnetic fields at my computer monitor screen are typically about 400 mG. One foot in front of the screen, the strongest field is only 4 mG. At 2 feet the field drops to 1 mG. This dependence on distance suggests one of the simplest of prudent avoidance methods: keep your distance.

When you rotate a single-axis meter to find the strongest reading, you should try to keep the center of the coil in one place. That way you'll be registering only changes in direction and not changes in distance.

Checking Your Home

The traditional home has three potential EMF sources to check:

↪ Exterior power lines

↪ Interior wiring system

↪ Electrical appliances

DO IT
Using a Single-Axis Meter
If you have a single-axis meter, place it up against a computer monitor or television, as shown in Figure 2-3. (The meter shown in the figure has the direction of the coil marked on its case.) Then try rotating the meter, as shown in the figure, and see what sort of measurements you get. For example, I obtained readings ranging from 8 mG to 180 mG at one location on my monitor. The larger number is the truer measurement of the field.

It's best to approach making your EMF measurements systematically. The first step is to make a sketch, to scale, of your home and lot. If power lines pass nearby, you may want to extend your sketch to include them. Be sure to show the electrical service drop for your home, that is, show where the electric service lines enter your home. Power may come from overhead cables or an underground service. If you know where the water lines are, include them in the drawing because the pipes may carry electrical

Figure 2-3 Magnetic fields are directional

current if they are used for grounding. Your sketch might look something like Figure 2-4. Depending on the size of your lot, you might want to make separate exterior and interior drawings. Then you can proceed to making the EMF measurements.

OUTSIDE THE HOME

The aims of the outdoor readings are (1) to determine sources of magnetic fields and (2) to see how the fields change with distance. Begin by making a systematic survey. There are a couple of common approaches to this exploratory phase.

One method is to mark a grid on your sketch, with the gridlines intersecting every 5 or 10 feet. Then take a measure-

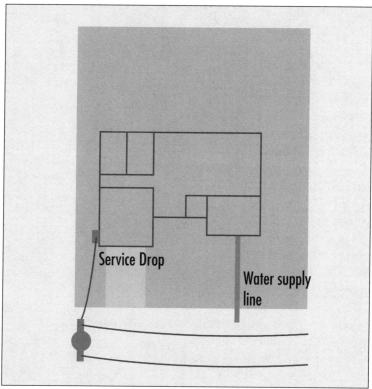

Figure 2-4 A sample home and lot sketch

ment at each intersection, recording it on your map. If you're using a single-axis meter, remember to orient the meter in various directions in order to find the largest reading.

The second method, suggested in a protocol provided by the California Department of Health Services (CDHS), is a little quicker. All measurements should be taken three feet above the ground.1) Take a measurement at each of the opposing four corners of the house. (2) Step 3 feet diagonally away from each corner and take a measurement. (3) Starting at one corner, step 6 feet away from the corner on a line perpendicular to one wall. Continue taking measurements each 6 feet in this direction until you reach the edge of your lot. Then repeat the process on a line perpendicular to the second wall at that corner. Finally, repeat this whole process at each of the other corners. (See Figure 2-5 for details.)

Next you should map known potential sources, such as the service drop, nearby distribution lines (on poles or underground), and underground water pipes. To find how distance affects the strength, take a reading directly over or under the suspected source, then move away at right angles to the line or pipe, taking readings every 6 feet.

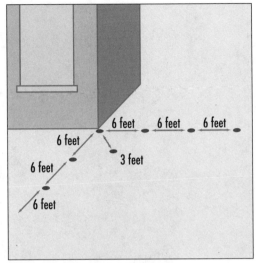

Figure 2-5 Taking outdoor readings

The fields produced by electrical distribution lines depend on the amount of current being carried. If you are diligent, you may want to test a particular location several times during the course of a day and night to see if there are significant variations in your neighborhood.

You may find a strong field with no obvious source. The CDHS protocol states, "Ground currents and unusual household wiring can lead to situations where source identification is impossible even after many hours of effort by trained engineers." One thing you can do in such a situation is turn off the main power switch to your home. If the magnetic field disappears, it has something to do with your house's wiring system. If the magnetic field is not affected, it's coming from an external source.

INSIDE THE HOME

Make a room-by-room survey. To get an overall picture of what's going on in your house, take a reading at the geometric center of each room, 3 feet above the floor, and record the result. (Single-axis-meter users, remember to try various meter orientations.) Keep in mind that the level of electrical activity can affect your readings. You might want to note if turning the lights on and off makes a difference. (Normally it doesn't.)

Next you should measure some special locations. You probably spend more time in bed than at any other single location, so measure the field there, about 8 inches above the center of the bed. The most likely location for a strong field is near the electrical service entrance because all the current to the house passes through that location. So find the location inside the house that is closest to the service drop and measure the field there. You may want to note how this reading is affected by such things as the refrigerator going on or by turning on an electric stove. Then, identify those locations at which you and your family spend the most time, and measure the fields there.

One advantage of making your own measurements is that you can spend as much time as you like on the project. So you can go beyond the usual protocol and thoroughly check every part of your house. Since wiring and water pipes can be EMF sources (see Chapter 3), you might want to pay particular attention to floor and wall areas near known wiring and water pipes.

ELECTRICAL APPLIANCES

Now you can turn your attention to the various electric appliances and other electrical devices in your home. The CDHS suggests taking readings at a distance of 4 inches and a distance of 18 inches from an operating appliance. (Note that the distance is the distance to the sensing coil in the meter.)

These measurements are going to be difficult to get accurately because the fields are not symmetrical or uniform. Even small variations in locations and meter orientations can produce large variations in your readings. Keep in mind, however, that the main goal here is to get *representative* values. So experiment: move the meter around to different sides of the appliance, try different meter orientations until you find the highest reading. Most likely you'll get different results on different sides of an appliance. Your goal is to get a rough idea of the strength of the field, so don't worry about moderate variations in the readings. The Electric Power Research Institute (EPRI) suggests taking readings at 3, 12, and 24 inches. Again, the main goal is to get an idea of how large the fields are and of how quickly they diminish with distance. Because appliance fields weaken so rapidly with distance, and their use is relatively infrequent, they contribute little to the overall EMF fields in a home. Some electrical devices, however, merit special attention.

Televisions and Computer Monitors

Televisions and computer monitors typically create stronger fields to the sides and to the back than they do to the front of the screen. This usually is more important for computer monitors—they are more likely to be situated so that human activity may be taking place to the side or back of them. Incidentally, when you hold the meter close to a screen, you may feel the hairs on the back of your hand rise. This effect has nothing to do with EMFs. It's a static electricity effect stemming from the way televisions and monitors work. It's also responsible for the amazing ability of the screen to attract dust to itself.

Electric Blankets and Heating Pads

Older electric blankets and heating pads are likely EMF culprits because of the way they are wired. Since these are in direct contact with your body, you should take readings with the meter lying on the surface and also at a distance of about 4 inches. Single-axis-meter users should rotate the meter until finding the maximum reading.

Electric Motors

Electric motors generate a lot of EMFs, so check things like electric drills, food processors, ceiling fans, appliance fans, refrigerators, electric can openers, vacuum cleaners, electric shavers, and electric hair dryers. Even an electric pencil sharpener can generate 1,000 mG at a distance of 4 inches.Cordless devices, such as cordless drills, generate much weaker EMFs than their AC counterparts.

An electric clock motor, at least those run by AC rather than from a battery, can generate modest fields in the range of 20 mG 4 inches from the clock. However, these fields are present continuously, instead of for just brief instances of usage.

Transformers

Transformers, which are devices that convert electricity from one voltage to another, are another likely source. They're partially responsible for TV EMFs, for example. Other places that may have transformers include door bells, fluorescent lights, and microwave ovens.

Microwaves

Don't confuse microwaves with EMFs. Several years ago there were concerns about microwave ovens leaking microwaves, and, if you were worried, you could buy a meter to check for such leaks. The microwaves are generated by a device called a klystron tube. The EMF fields come from the transformer and from motors.

Heat Producers

Devices that use electricity to produce heat generally draw large currents and are potential EMF sources. So check

APPLIANCE	AT 4 INCHES	AT 12 INCHES	AT 36 INCHES
blender	50 – 200	5 – 20	0.3 – 1
can opener	1300 – 4000	31 – 280	0.5 – 7.0
drill	350 – 500	20 – 30	0.8 – 2.0
electric shaver	14 – 1600	0.8 – 90	<0.1 – 3
fluorescent fixture	40 – 120	2 – 30	<0.1 – 3
hair dryer	3 – 1400	<0.1 – 70	<0.1 – 3
iron	12 – 45	1 – 3	0.1 – 0.2
television	5 – 100	0.4 – 20	<0.1 – 1.5
toaster	10 – 60	0.6 – 7.0	<0.1
vacuum cleaner	230 – 1300	20 – 180	1 – 20

Table 2-1 Sample magnetic fields in milligauss

electric toasters, electric stoves, electric heaters, and the like.

Table 2-1 shows some typical values for some appliances. Note the large variations. These reflect differences between different designs as well as other variables, such as settings and exactly where the field is measured. Also note that most of the fields are very weak at a distance of 36 inches. Appendix C provides a more extensive table.

The Next Step

Once you've made EMF readings in your home and on your property, you may find your worries have been lessened. Or you may feel that you need to take some sort of action. The next chapter looks into how to reduce your exposure to EMFs.

Lowering EMFs

Suppose you've identified EMF sources in your home. What do you do next? The answers, of course, depend upon what you've found. We can classify sources into three groups: electrical appliances, internal sources coming from the house's wiring and grounding systems, and external sources, coming from the power company's transmission and distribution lines. We'll look at each in turn.

Electrical Appliances

The basic rule for dealing with EMFs from electrical appliances—such as kitchen appliances, power tools, computers, and electric blankets— is simple: *keep your distance!* EMFs weaken rapidly with distance. My computer monitor, for example, produces a field of 400 mG 4 inches from the screen. At 12 inches the field drops to 4 mG. So don't snuggle up to your TV or microwave. If an offending clock or radio is near your head when you sleep, move it a bit further away. If you have a fluorescent desk lamp, keep your distance or replace it with a standard incandescent lamp. Although it's much less efficient, it is much lower in EMF emissions.

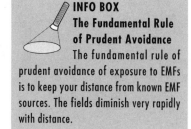

INFO BOX
The Fundamental Rule of Prudent Avoidance
The fundamental rule of prudent avoidance of exposure to EMFs is to keep your distance from known EMF sources. The fields diminish very rapidly with distance.

Unfortunately you can't always keep your distance. For instance, holding an electric shaver 24 inches from your skin doesn't produce a very close shave. In a case like that, you have to decide if the as yet unknown risk of using the razor a few minutes a day outweighs its convenience to you. If you think it does, you can switch to a blade razor or else revert to a more hirsute state.

In some cases you can modify your behavior to reduce exposure. For example, when using a blender or a can opener, stand back when operating it. If you have a magnetic meter, you might find the field is weaker in some directions than in others. In that case you can position yourself or the appliance so that you're in the weak field area. Make sure that your children don't hang around the microwave oven door, watching what's going on inside. Make sure they don't get too close to the television.

ELECTRIC BLANKETS

Electric blankets have been redesigned to reduce EMF emissions. The electric blanket case is particularly interesting because the principle behind the change is simple and also applies to house wiring and to power lines. Let's take a look.

The magnetic field produced by a current through a straight wire circles the wire. Figure 3-1 shows current flowing along a wire directed into the page. If the current in the wire is AC, then the magnetic field is fluctuating, dropping to zero when the current drops to zero and reversing direction when the current reverses. (Chapter 6 discusses this in more detail.)

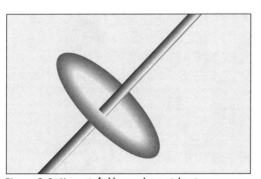

Figure 3-1 Magnetic field around a straight wire

Turning on an electric appliance creates a closed loop, called a closed circuit, through which the electric current flows. The current flows from the power plant, through the appliance, and back to the power plant. The current flowing into the device equals the current coming out. (The "in" and "out" reverse as the current reverses.) Suppose, then, we arrange the circuitry so that the outgoing current is carried parallel to and alongside the incoming current. In this case the two wires produce magnetic fields in opposite directions, so they nearly cancel each other out. This pairing of wires is what electric blanket manufactures have done for their newer models, and this simple manufacturing change has cut down EMFs by about 95 percent from older designs, in which oppositely directed currents weren't paired. Figure 3-2 shows this cancellation. In the figure current is flowing into the page on the right and out of the page on the left. The magnetic field lines are closely packed between the wires and near the wires, indicating the field is strong there. The spacing between the field lines increases rapidly farther away from the wires, indicating the fields quickly weaken far from the wires because of the cancellation effect.

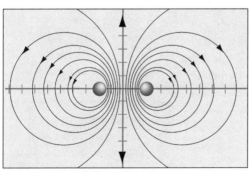

Figure 3-2 Partial field cancellation for currents in opposite directions

COMPUTER MONITORS

Computer monitors (video display terminals, or VDTs) have

also been redesigned, although they are much more complex than electric blankets. The monitor uses high voltage to fire a beam of electrons at the screen. A coil produces a magnetic field that deflects the beam horizontally, sweeping it back and forth across the screen, producing a horizontal line that forms part of the image. Another coil deflects the beam vertically, forming the successive lines that produce the whole image. A power transformer converts AC power to the required DC (direct current) power. Another transformer provides the high-frequency signal (15,000 Hz to 45,000 Hz, or, as it's usually written, 15 kHz to 45 kHz) needed to control the horizontal beam. As a result of all these things, a monitor produces a range of emissions. Some are in the 50 Hz to 90 Hz range of ELF (Extra Low Frequency) emissions that we've been dubbing EMFs. The 15 kHz to 45 kHz emissions fall in the province of VLF (Very Low Frequency) emissions. Thus a monitor produces emissions that many EMF meters won't pick up.

You may be wondering why high frequencies like 45,000 Hz are called Very Low Frequency. It's a matter of the frame of reference. Compared to radio waves and microwaves, 45,000 Hz *is* a very low frequency. But it's high compared to 60-Hz EMFs. Since engineers had already used the VLF label for the 45,000 Hz frequencies, they had to resort to Extra Low Frequency to describe 60-Hz fields.

Many manufacturers now produce monitors with reduced emissions. In particular, monitors may claim compliance with the Swedish MPR II standard for monitor emissions. Table 3-1 summarizes the magnetic portion of the 1991 MPR II standard. Each value represents the average of measurements at 48 standard measurement points. Also, each value represents the combined strength of the magnetic fields in the indicated frequency ranges. In addition, the

INFO BOX
Computer Monitors
The electronics in a computer monitor generate many frequencies of electromagnetic fields, ranging from the 60-Hz range up to several thousand Hz. Thus recent concerns about the safety of monitors go beyond the ELF range (60 Hz to 2,000 Hz) to include the VLF (Very Low Frequency) range (2,000 Hz and higher).

MAGNETIC FIELD FREQUENCY RANGE	MAXIMUM FIELD STRENGTH
Band I: 5 Hz – 2,000 Hz	2.5 mG
Band II: 2 kHz– 400 kHz	0.25 mG

Table 3-1 The Swedish MPR II standard for magnetic radiation

Swedish standard places limits on the electric field in the ELF realm and the VLF realm and on X-ray radiation.

If you have a monitor with high measured EMF magnetic fields and want to reduce emissions, one recourse is to purchase a new monitor that meets the Swedish MPR II standards. If possible, you should see if you can bring a EMF meter to a showroom and take measurements of a prospective purchase to make sure it really is significantly better than what you have.

Another alternative is to retrofit your current monitor. Here you have to exercise some caution. Many manufacturers sell screens that cut glare and provide electromagnetic shielding. These screens reduce VLF electromagnetic fields; but at ELF frequencies, such devices shield just *electric* fields, not *magnetic* fields. At the time of this writing, the only tested device offering protection from EMF magnetic fields is the NoRad ELF Protect. This device is not a screen. Rather it looks a bit like a set of headphones spanning the sides and top of a monitor. It's made of an alloy that pulls magnetic fields into itself. The net effect is to reduce magnetic emissions in all directions by about 50 percent to 70 percent, enough to make many noncompliant monitors meet the Swedish standard for magnetic fields. Figure 3-3 shows a monitor with a glass shield and a monitor with the ELF Protect.

A television set, of course, has the same basic design as a computer monitor. Normally, televisions pose less EMF risk than monitors because people typically view TVs at a much greater distance. (Remember EMFs weaken rapidly with distance.) Just be sure that you or your children don't get too close to the television. Viewing a set from a distance

 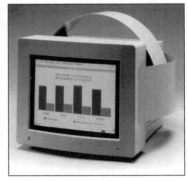

Figure 3-3 Reducing monitor emissions with NoRad UltraGlass and ELF Protect

of five feet or greater should make your exposure to TV EMFs inconsequential.

Wiring and Grounding

Appliances generally produce EMFs just in their near vicinity. If you find EMFs elsewhere in your house, they most likely come from your home's wiring and grounding system or from the outside. One way to test what's going on is to turn off the electric power to your house. If the EMFs go away, your problem comes from the house. If they stay, they come from the outside. If the readings drop but still are high, then you have contributions from both. If you have readings that are high just in certain places, such as near the service drop, you can move commonly used furniture away from the sites. In other cases more drastic measures may be needed.

INTRODUCTION TO WIRING

To understand what can cause problems, you need to take a look at how homes are wired. Modern homes use three-wire wiring. One wire, the *ground,* is grounded locally. For example, it can be connected to a copper rod driven into the

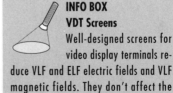

INFO BOX
VDT Screens
Well-designed screens for video display terminals reduce VLF and ELF electric fields and VLF magnetic fields. They don't affect the ELF magnetic fields that we've termed EMFs.

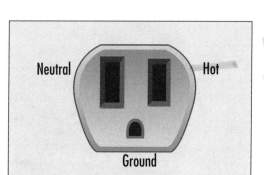

Figure 3-4 A standard electrical outlet

ground. In a three-hole outlet, the round hole connects to the ground wire. Normally the ground wire carries no current. It's there to allow you to ground electrical equipment plugged into the outlet. This reduces the risk of electrical shocks. The other two wires carry the current. One wire, the *hot* wire, is connected to the short slot in a standard electrical outlet. The other wire, the *neutral* wire, is connected to the long slot (see Figure 3-4). The standard color coding practice is that the ground wire is green, the neutral wire is white, and the hot wire is black. All three are sheathed together.

Voltage is a measure of electric pressure, of how strongly current is pushed through a wire. Voltage always is measured between two locations, that is, voltmeters really measure voltage differences. For instance, the voltage between the hot and neutral wires typically oscillates between +120 V and –120 V. (Actually, the 120 V value is a kind of average value; the instantaneous peak values are closer to 170 V.) The neutral wire, like the ground wire, is grounded, and ground usually is taken as the zero point for voltage measurements. Thus we think of the neutral wire as maintaining a zero voltage as the voltage on the hot wire varies from –120 V to +120 V. The primary difference between the neutral wire and the ground wire is that the neutral wire is part of the circuit and carries current. The ground wire shouldn't carry current unless there has been some sort of electrical failure. Ideally the neutral and the hot wire in a circuit carry the identical current. One carries the current into a device and the other receives the return current, which will be the same unless some charges leaked out of the device. The idea is the same as for a car radiator. The amount of water pushed into the radiator by the water pump should equal the amount leaving the other end unless there is a leak. One difference is that alternating current flows first in one direction, then the other. Nonetheless the current in the neutral wire usually is termed the return current. It also is called the *neutral* current.

As you saw when we discussed electric blankets, you can reduce EMF emissions by pairing wires having identical currents running in opposite directions. Modern wiring code, by keeping the hot wire and neutral wire together, accomplishes this end.

Prior to the three-wire system, homes used a two-wire system. This system also kept the hot and neutral wires together, thus minimizing EMF emissions.

Several things can mess up the ideal wiring system. Let's look at some of them now.

IN DEPTH
The Ground Wire
If the hot and neutral wires carry all the current, what's the ground wire for? Suppose you have just the hot and the neutral wires, and you have a computer with a metal case plugged into an ungrounded outlet. If a hot wire inside the computer gets loose and touches the case. and then *you* touch the case, *you* can get a severe shock. Now suppose the computer is plugged into a grounded circuit and the case is connected to the ground wire. In this case, if the hot wire touches the case, there will be a short circuit to ground, which will blow a fuse or trip a circuit breaker before you get a chance to electrocute yourself.

UNPAIRED WIRES

One route to higher EMFs is to separate the hot wire from the neutral wire. In this case you don't get the partial cancellation you get from paired wires. This has two adverse effects:

↪ The magnetic field is stronger

↪ The magnetic field doesn't decrease as rapidly with increasing distance

For example, suppose a paired wire produced a field of 2 mG at 1 foot. At 10 feet the field would drop to one-hundredth of that value, 0.02 mG. Now suppose you had a sin-

CURRENT CARRIER	PAIRED WIRES	SINGLE WIRE
Field at 1 foot	2 mG	100 mG
Field at 10 feet	0.02 mG	10 mG

Table 3-2 Magnetic fields produced by paired wires and a single wire carrying the same electric current

gle wire carrying the same current. It would produce a magnetic field of 100 mG at 10 feet. Furthermore, at 10 feet the field would only drop by a factor of 10, down to 10 mG. So at a distance of 1 foot, the single wire produced a field 50 times stronger than paired wires carrying the same current. At 10 feet the single wire produced a field 500 times stronger than the paired wires! Table 3-2 summarizes these results. As you can see, unpaired wiring can really raise EMF levels.

How can you get unpaired wiring? First, a house may not have been wired according to code. For example, one can simplify some wiring problems, such as controlling one light with two switches, by using unpaired wiring. Second, paired wiring wasn't always part of the electrical code. Many houses built before World War II used something called *knob and tube* wiring, in which the hot wires and neutral wires were strung separately.

About the only inexpensive thing you can do for these kinds of wiring problems is to try to position beds and chairs where the fields are weakest. The real solution is to have a knowledgeable electrician fix or replace the wiring, but that won't come cheap.

GROUNDING PROBLEMS

The field cancellation produced by paired wires works as long as both wires carry the same current: the return current balances the current coming in. But the grounding system may destroy that balance by di-

> **INFO BOX**
> **Outlet Testers**
> Most hardware store carry inexpensive (under $10) outlet testers that plug into the standard three-hole socket. Colored lights on the tester indicate wiring errors such as hot and neutral wires that have been connected to the wrong terminal and ungrounded ground wires .

verting some return current from the neutral wire into the ground, perhaps along a water pipe. Then the reduced current in the neutral wire counteracts only part of the incoming current. For instance, suppose the hot wire carries 10 amps (*amp* is short for *ampere,* the unit used to measure electric current), and that 1 amp leaks into the ground and escapes along a water pipe. That leaves 9 amps in the neutral wire, which acts to cancel the EMFs produced by 9 amps in the hot wire. That leaves 1 amp in the hot wire unbalanced, and that 1 amp of unbalanced current produces much stronger EMFs than the remaining 9 balanced amps. Also the metal water pipe carryinng away the leaked current acts like another unbalanced, uncancelled, single-wire source.

To see how this can happen, let's start with an idealized case in which the neutral wire is grounded at the power station. In this case the only places the current can flow are through the hot wire and through the neutral wire, so the currents through the two wires will balance. (The current in the neutral line often is called the *return current,* but keep in mind that the current flows in both directions in an AC system.) The problem is that the neutral wire at your home most likely will have a voltage difference compared to the local ground. One reason is that all wires have at least some resistance, and this produces a voltage drop when current runs through them. This would result in the neutral wire having a voltage difference relative to the ground at your location, which would be a potential safety hazard. Therefore the neutral line also is grounded at your end, typically through a grounding rod at the power pole and a grounding rod at your service drop. This causes some of the current that otherwise would flow through the neutral wire to and from the power station to flow through the earth instead. The ground provides an alternative path for current to return to the power plant. If your water system uses metal pipes, the pipes can wind up carrying much of that ground, or stray return, current.

Next, within the home, the neutral wire may be grounded at one or more locations to water pipes. Once again, there can be a voltage difference in the neutral wire between where it is grounded at the service entrance and where it's grounded to a water pipe. This can produce unbalanced currents in the house wires as well as a current in the pipe (see Figure 3-5). Also, if the whole water district system is metal and if some of its pipes pass near the power station, the pipes might look like one big alternative neutral wire to the electrical system. In that case a substantial part of the current may choose to travel by pipe instead of by wire. Your pipes may even wind up with stray return currents from neighboring properties. If you find that an EMF meter lets you trace the routes of water pipes in your house or on your property, you'll know that they are carrying part of the neutral line current. If your home uses plastic pipes, you don't have to worry about plumbing line currents, because plastic doesn't conduct electricity.

The American Water Works Association frowns upon the practice of grounding circuits to metal water pipes because it can create a shock hazard to water utility workers and promote corrosion and other chemical activity in the pipes. On the other hand, some local building codes mandate that the circuit be grounded to metal water pipes in order to decrease risks of shocks and short circuits. In short, multiple grounding reduces electrical risks but increases the likelihood of unbalanced current flow in the wires and hence increases the likelihood of high EMF levels.

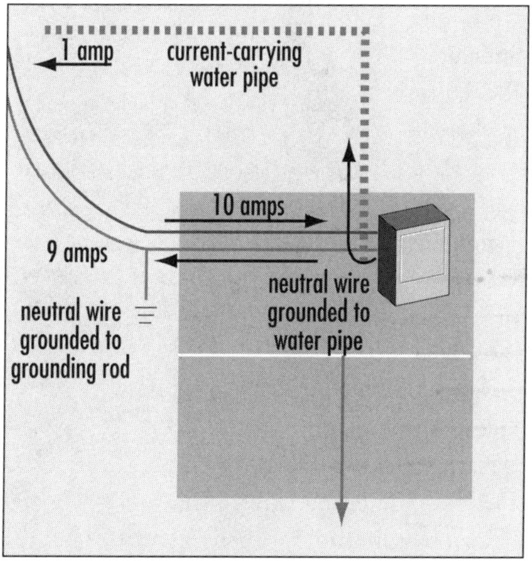

What can you do if diverted neutral currents are a problem

1 amp ← current-carrying water pipe

10 amps →

9 amps

neutral wire grounded to grounding rod

neutral wire grounded to water pipe

Figure 3-5 Multiple grounding in a home

for you? That depends on your local codes. They may permit an electrician to modify the grounding system so that you don't leak electric current into the water pipes. Another possibility is that a plumber can install a dielectric union joining your water supply pipe to the water district system. This is a short nonconducting connector that isolates your pipes electrically from the rest of the system, blocking the flow of electricity through them.

Eliminating the plumbing path for stray return current helps you two ways. First, since the water supply pipe can combine return currents from several grounds, it may have a larger current than the unbalanced current in individual paired wires. This can make the pipe the largest single contributor to EMFs in the home. Second, by eliminating the pipe option, you keep the return current in the neutral wire, where it belongs, and keep the paired-wire cancellation system working.

A long-term option may be changing the building codes. Japan and some European countries use an electrical safety system that reduces or eliminates local grounding. Instead, they use ground-fault inter-

> ⚡ **DO IT**
> **Measuring the Neutral Voltage**
> Here's something you can do if you meet the following conditions:
>
> 1. You have a voltmeter capable of measuring 120 V AC voltages.
>
> 2. You know how to use the meter.
>
> 3. You have three-hole electric outlets.
>
> Use the meter to measure the voltage difference between the ground wire (the round hole in the outlet) and the neutral wire (the longer of the two slots). If you try this on a circuit that's not currently in use (no pun intended), you probably will get close to a zero reading since both are grounded. Next, plug something that uses a lot of current, say a toaster, into the same circuit. When you turn the toaster on, you'll see the voltage difference between the ground and neutral wire increase, perhaps to a volt or so. The current running through the neutral wire produces a voltage difference between the plug and where the wire is grounded. The larger the current and the greater the distance from where the neutral wire is grounded, the bigger this voltage will be. If you were to ground the neutral wire at your end of the line, this voltage difference would divert some of the current into the ground, unbalancing the original circuit.

rupters (GFIs) to protect against electrical risks. A GFI monitors the currents in the hot and neutral wires. If the two currents get out of balance, that means that there is a current leak or a short circuit somewhere. In that case the

GFI breaks the circuit. In the U.S., many building codes for new construction require GFI outlets for certain locations, such as near sinks. Such outlets cost under $10 but a are slightly trickier to install than regular outlets. However, the U.S. does not yet have an integrated strategy for reducing local grounding.

External Sources

The third class of EMF sources are those outside the house. The usual external sources are the electric power transmission lines and distribution lines. The transmission lines are the high-voltage lines used to transfer electric power from the generating sites to substations. The substations transform the power to lower voltages, which are used by the primary distribution lines. These are the wires you see at the top of local utility poles, attached to the pole by porcelain insulators. Some poles will carry transformers that convert the primary distribution power to 115 V or 230 V. The secondary distribution lines carry power at these voltages. Secondary distribution lines run from pole to pole (mounted lower than the primary distribution lines) and from pole to your service drop. In some areas the primary and secondary distribution lines are carried underground.

If you find that transmission lines are producing high fields on your property, you can ask your utility company to inspect them. You may have an easily corrected problem, such as a nearby power pole with a faulty transformer or faulty grounding. Or you may have to take some sort of community or legal action. We won't go into those areas, but we will look a little into the sorts of problems that might arise and what electric utilities can do about them. That way, if you are concerned with public policy, you'll have some idea of what's involved. First let's review the situation.

POWER LINES

The magnetic fields produced by power lines depend on the current carried by the lines and on the line geometry. That is, the closer a hot line is to the line carrying its return current, the better cancellation you get. The hot wire-neutral wire model we discussed for home wiring doesn't apply to transmission lines. They use something called three-phase AC. The details aren't important here. The main points to know are (1) the current for a three-phase circuit is carried through three wires instead of two, and (2) you can get partial field cancellation from a three-wire set by grouping the three wires close to one another. Note that this three-wire system is different from the three-wire home system we discussed. In the home system, only two wires actually carried current, and the third served to ground devices plugged into the circuit. In transmission lines all three wires carry current.

Three factors determine the EMFs you get from power lines. First, the higher the current in a power line, the greater the EMFs. Second, the more closely spaced a set of wires are, the more effective the cancellation. Third, currents that return through the ground create unbalanced currents in the power lines, increasing EMFs.

The Role of Voltage

Most people jump to the conclusion that if a 115-V line produces EMFs, then a 115,000-V line must be a 1,000 times more hazardous. It doesn't work that way because what counts in producing magnetic fields is the current, not the voltage. A 10-amp current produces a 20-mG magnetic field at a distance of 1 meter regardless of the voltage of the line. However, the same current provides more power at higher voltages. If a power company switched from 115,000 V to 115 V for its transmission lines, it would have to use much larger currents. For example, suppose a company had to supply a

INFO BOX
Birds on the Wire
Often you'll see birds blithely perched on uninsulated high-voltage wires, and you may have wondered why they don't come to grief. The reason is that high voltages in themselves are not harmful. What is harmful is the high currents that these voltages can produce in a body. But to get a current, the body has to provide a path connecting two different voltages. Then the current flows from the higher voltage to the lower voltage. The birds on a power line are in no danger unless they simultaneously touch something else. For example, a bird that simultaneously touched its wings to two power lines would be killed. From the avian standpoint, therefore, it's better to have large spacing between transmission wires.

VOLTAGE	AMPERES NEEDED TO TRANSMIT 10 MEGAWATTS OF POWER	MAGNETIC FIELDS AT 100 METERS (110 YARDS)
115,000	87	1.7 mG
115	87,000	1,740 mG

Table 3-3 Currents and magnetic fields for high- and low-voltage lines

small community with 10 megawatts of power. The company could meet this need with a 115,000-V system carrying 87 amperes of current, or with a 115-V system carrying 87,000 amperes! So in terms of reducing magnetic EMFs, high-voltage transmission lines are big winners, as Table 3-3 illustrates. (The table assumes a single wire with no cancellation from other wires.)

Using high voltages also greatly reduces the power lost in the transmission, because power loss is proportional to the square of the current. That means that doubling the current carried by a power line quadruples the power lost. Making the current ten times bigger makes the power loss 100 times bigger. Using 115-V transmission lines instead of 115,000-V lines would increase the amount of wasted power by a factor of 1 million! This is why power companies use high voltage for transmission lines.

From the EMF perspective, the disadvantage to using high-voltage lines is that the different lines have to be kept far apart from each other. If two lines are too close, you get very intense electric fields between the wires that ionize the air and make the air an electric conductor. Then you can get power discharged into the ionized air *(corona discharge)* and possibly get electricity arcing over from one line to another *(flashover)*. The separation of the lines reduces the cancellation effect.

Transmission Line Design

Traditionally transmission lines have not been designed with field cancellation in mind. Figure 3-6 shows a typical configuration. It carries one three-phase circuit on the left side, and one three-phase circuit on the right. (The phases are labeled A, B, and C.) The differently phased wires are widely spaced, so cancellation is less effective than it can be.

You can improve cancellation by changing the phase connections as shown in Figure 3-7. By pairing the A phase with the C phase and vice versa, this configuration reduces the magnetic fields by 50 percent or more. This kind of alteration is comparatively easy and inexpensive; the power company just has to change the wiring connections at the power station at one end of the transmission line and at the substations fed by the transmission line.

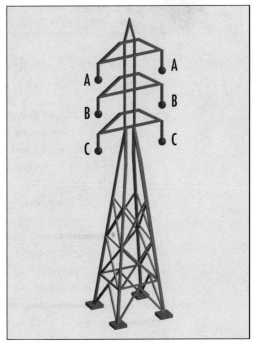

Figure 3-6 A traditional transmission power pole

Or, as shown in Figure 3-8, you can create a new design. This design, which arranges the three wires in a triangular configuration, is even more effective at canceling fields. Some power companies are beginning to use such designs for new power lines, but the reconnection method is a much cheaper way of handling existing distribution systems.

Designing power-transmission lines involves trade-offs. Bringing the wires closer to each other to decrease magnetic fields increases corona discharges, the sounds you hear from power lines, radio interference, and the likelihood of something (a kite, a large bird) connecting two lines and shorting them out. Increasing the voltage to reduce currents and magnetic fields increases the electric fields, which may have undesirable side effects, such as more noise, corona discharge, and greater likelihood of flashovers.

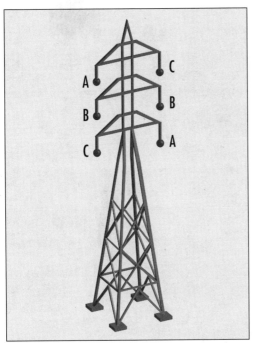

Figure 3-7 A traditional transmission power pole modified to reduce magnetic fields

Underground Lines

Another possibility is placing transmission lines underground. The advantage is that the wires, being placed in an oil-filled pipe, can be packed more closely together than in the air, and this cancels the magnetic fields more effectively. A disadvantage is the lines that are closer to people than they would be if strung on poles. In the case of unbalanced currents, underground transmission is worse than transmission using poles. That's because the unbalanced part of the current isn't affected by the cancellation process, so both underground and overhead lines would produce the same EMFs in that case. However, the underground lines would be closer to people and houses, making the local fields stronger. (The ground doesn't provide any magnetic shielding.) Underground lines also have economic and technical disadvantages.

DISTRIBUTION LINES

High-voltage transmission lines (69 kV to 765 kV) often are the source of community concerns because they are so visible and because we've all seen "Danger! High Voltage" signs. Indeed, flying a kite into a high-voltage line can be very dangerous. But from the EMF perspective, the lower-voltage distribution lines contribute more to most people's exposures to EMFs. The distribution lines come closer to our homes; and because the voltage is lower, they may carry larger currents, producing larger magnetic fields. Remember that utility poles typically carry the primary distribution lines, which have intermediate voltages in the 5 kV to 35 kV range, and the secondary lines, which have low voltages in the 115 V to 240 V range.

Exposure to Distribution System EMFs

Generally speaking, the further you are "downstream" from the power station on a primary distribution line system, the less exposure you get to EMFs from the primary

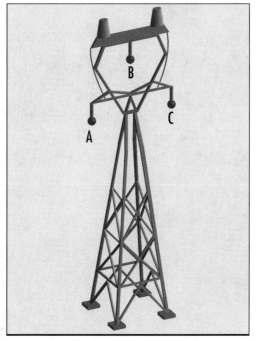

Figure 3-8 An EMF-aware transmission power pole design

distribution lines. That's because the electric current keeps getting subdivided as electricity is diverted to houses along the line. It's a lot like a pipeline system for delivering water. At one end, the pipe carries enough water to serve all the houses on the line. By the time the pipe reaches the end of line, it just carries the water used by the last house on the line. Similarly, in the case of power lines, exposure to primary distribution line EMFs would be strongest near the beginning of the line and weakest at the end, where the current would just be the current used by the last house.

The real situation is more complex because the main power is carried by the primary distribution lines at, say, 35,000 V. At the first house on the line, a transformer on the power pole converts some of the power to 240 V to supply the house. Usually the transformer will serve several houses. Because of the relationship between voltage and current, the 240-V lines may carry more current than the higher voltage lines. Thus it's likely that the low-voltage secondary distribution lines contribute more to most home's EMF exposure than do the mid-voltage primary distribution lines.

Summary

Three classes of sources affect EMF levels in your home:

↳ Electrical appliances

↳ Your home's wiring and grounding system

↳ Utility power lines

Electrical appliance EMFs are the simplest to manage because they weaken quickly with distance. Thus their effects are localized and, in many cases, all you have to do is stay two or three feet away from an appliance when it is in use. You can relocate some items so that they are more distant from locations such as your bed or your favorite easy chair. Table 2-1, Appendix C, and an EMF meter should give you a good idea of which devices have high EMFs.

The arm's-length approach isn't practical for all electrical devices, for instance, an electric shaver or an electric heating pad. If you are concerned about possible risks, then you may have to change your habits.

The way your home is wired and the way the wiring system is grounded may produce EMFs in your home. These EMFs usually rise from unbalanced electric currents and they are much less localized than appliance EMFs. Your recourse is to avoid the higher EMF areas, or to have the wiring and grounding redone,which is much more expensive.

In most cases utility power lines will be the weakest contributors to the EMF levels in a house. A power utility should fix faulty transformers and grounding problems. But if your complaint is with the siting or design of the power lines, your recourse may have to be community or legal action.

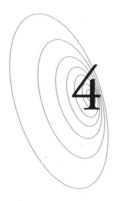

Risk

4

Now that you've seen the practical side of EMF management, let's take a deeper look at the background. This chapter begins that process by examining risk.

Who among us are the risk takers? The men and women who scale 2,000-foot granite rock faces? Race car drivers? People who fly kites in thunderstorms? Employees who offer humorous evaluations of a boss's intelligence? In truth we all are risk takers. For example, the odds are 175 in 1 million that you'll have a fatal accident during the course of one year. Do you walk around? The odds are 48 in 1 million that you'll have a fatal fall during the course of one year. Do you put stuff into your mouth? The odds are 11 in 1 million that you'll die from the ingestion of food or of some object during the course of one year. And there is about one chance in 10 million each year that the earth will be struck by an asteroid or comet large enough to cause a global catastrophe! The point of this little discussion is not to frighten you out of your wits; it's to point out that risk is an ever-present fact of life (see Figure 4-1). That being the case, it's useful to know some-

QUICK LOOK

Being at risk is an unavoidable aspect of life. Thus we usually have to judge which risks are acceptable and which are not. Statistics provide tools for evaluating the severity of risks, but there are important psychological aspects, too. This chapter looks into some of the objective and subjective aspects of risk evaluation.

thing about how peo-
ple come up with risk
statistics and how to
interpret them. It's
also interesting to see
how people respond
to risk information.
We'll take a quick
look at these topics in
this chapter.

Assessing Risk

For some situations
it is fairly simple to
assess risk. Consider
the risk of dying from
a fatal fall. According
to the National Safety
Council, about 12,200

Figure 4-1 Risk takers

Americans died from fatal falls in 1991. Dividing that by an
estimated 1991 population of 253 million gives a death rate
of 48 people per 1 million. Therefore you had 48 chances
in 1 million of having a fatal fall in 1991. Incidentally—
the death rate from falls was 83 out of 1 million in 1970, so
things have gotten better!

This approach, of course, oversimplifies matters by
lumping everyone into the same category. If you were to
gather more information, you would find fatal falls were
more common for some occupations and age groups than
for others. This points out an important fact about risk statistics: they apply to groups of people, not to individuals.
On the basis of statistics we can predict how many people
might die of falls each year. With more information, we
could predict how many people in various categories might
die. But statistics can only tell us how many people are affected in a given group, not *which* people.

EXPOSURE

Let's take a closer look at risk by examining a particular case: the risk of death by automobile accident. (This may not be your idea of fun, but it will help you understand risk concepts.) Expressing the risk in terms of deaths per capita ignores a very important factor: some people spend much more time in automobiles than others. That is, some people have more *exposure* to this particular risk than others. To take this into account, we can use the statistics a bit differently by describing the death rate in terms of miles traveled instead of in terms of the number of people. For instance, in 1989 Americans traveled over 2 trillion passenger miles. (Passenger miles are computed by multiplying the distance a car travels by the number of people it carries. A car going 10 miles with one occupant produces 10 passenger miles, while a car going 10 miles with 4 occupants produces 40 passenger miles.) There were just under 25,000 passenger deaths in 1989, which can be expressed as 1.1 deaths per 100 million passenger miles.

How can we use this statistic? The usual way is to make the simplifying assumption that the risk of an accident depends only upon the miles driven, ignoring other factors such as health, age, personality type, and so on. To find the risk factor for a particular person, multiply the death rate by the miles traveled. For instance, suppose Emmy travels 10,000 miles per year. Then the odds that she will have a fatal accident are

10,000 miles x 1.1 deaths/100,000,000 miles = 1.1 / 10,000.

That is, Emmy has 1.1 chances in 10,000 of making an encounter of the fatal kind. Next, consider Oscar, who travels 100,000 miles a year. His chances of having a fatal accident are

100,000 miles x 1.1 deaths/100,000,000 miles = 1.1 / 1,000.

That is, he has 1.1 chances in 1,000 of experimenting with the afterlife. In short, Oscar has ten times the exposure as Emmy to the risk of having a fatal automobile accident.

Risk is not a yes/no matter. Your degree of risk depends on your level of exposure to the hazard.

Most of the statistics in this chapter are taken from Mark S. Hoffman, editor, *The World Almanac and Book of Facts* (New York: Pharos Books, 1993). The death rates for passenger miles, however, are from the 1992 edition.

Scientists have yet to determine what the most meaningful measure of exposure is to EMFs. The amount of time one spends in a field and the strength of the field most likely are important, but there may be other factors such as the strength of the local geomagnetic field and whether the field fluctuates a lot. This will be discussed in more detail in Chapter 5.

INDIRECT CAUSES

Assessing risk becomes trickier when we deal with processes that don't cause death directly. For instance, low-level X-rays won't kill you outright, but they can increase the likelihood that you will get cancer. How do you go about establishing links between, say, X-rays, smoking, and EMFs on the one hand, and cancer on the other?

One poor approach is personal experience. You've probably heard claims along the lines of the following: "My great uncle Thor smoked a pack a day and lived to 102, when he was shot by a jealous husband. So don't tell me that smoking causes lung cancer!" Of course, someone else might respond this way: "My cousin Juno smoked a pack a day and got lung cancer at the age of 36, so don't tell me that smoking doesn't cause lung cancer!" Such anecdotal claims prove nothing, because you can't distinguish between a coincidence and a relationship with just one or two cases.

Scientific studies usually fall into one of two groups: studies that examine statistics looking for connections, and studies that look for mechanisms that would explain connections. Let's look at the statistical approach first. For example, find out what percentage of lung cancer victims were heavy smokers, light smokers, and nonsmokers. Then compare those results to the relative number of heavy smokers, light smokers, and nonsmokers in the population at large. If heavy smokers are more common among lung cancer victims than among the population at large, you've established a connection between smoking and lung cancer.

The epidemiological studies mentioned in Chapters 1 and 5 are examples of statistical studies. Epidemiological studies can take a long time. It took many years for the connection between low-level radioactive radiation and cancer to show up. Statistical studies don't always give quick answers.

STATISTICS AND CAUSE AND EFFECT

Establishing a connection does not mean that there must be a cause-and-effect relationship. For example, recently there has been some controversy about whether EMFs from cellular phones can cause brain cancer. At this time there is not enough information to determine if there is a relationship or not. For the sake of argument, suppose that the data eventually shows a connection between brain cancer and cellular phone users. There still would be other possible explanations than cause and effect. For example, it might turn out that brain cancer is related to stress and that cellular phone users, on the average, lead more stressful lives than most people. Stress would be what statisticians call a *confounding factor*. To determine if stress were the true cause would require more studies, studies that compared cellular phone users with nonusers having similar stress levels. That is, you need a control group, a group of

IN DEPTH
Confounding Factors
Confounding factors muddle the ability of statistical studies to detect relationships. The idea is that there may be some unconsidered factor that is the real cause of the observed relationship. Consider the Denver findings (Chapter 5, *EMF Research*) that correlated EMF exposure to childhood leukemia. Suppose, for example, that it turned out that the high-exposure homes in Denver were, on the average, in lower-income areas than the low-exposure homes. Then it might be the low income rather than the high exposure to EMFs that increased the cancer risk. To check that possibility, you would have to do further studies that took income into account. Once you think of a confounding factor, you can test to see if it has an effect, but it's difficult to know if you've thought of all possible confounding factors. And the more you do think of, the more studies you have to make.

people who don't use cellular phones but who otherwise are as stressed as the cellular phone users. Suppose it turned out that among people with equally stressful lives, cellular phone users were more prone to cancer. That would eliminate stress as the sole cause, but there could be some other factor that's the culprit. Or it might turn out that stress is a *cofactor*, that is, that stress and EMFs together cause the problem. This is just a hypothetical example, but it shows some of the problems with statistical studies.

STATISTICS AND SAMPLE SIZE

Suppose a study finds that EMFs increase the risk of childhood leukemia by a factor of two. The strength of that conclusion depends upon the sample size. To see how that works, let's consider a less emotionally loaded example: flipping a coin.

The laws of probability tell us that if you toss ten coins, you should expect to get five heads and five tails, on the average. The phrase "on the average" is crucial. If you actually toss ten coins, you might get seven heads, or perhaps just four heads, or rarely no heads. Random variations like this always show up in statistical happenings. But if you tossed ten coins a hundred times, you'd find that the average number of heads per toss of ten was pretty close to five, providing the coins were fair.

Now consider the following problem. A friend has a machine for making special coins used for the coin toss in sporting events. She wants to know if the machine is producing fair, unbiased coins. You toss a coin twice, and it comes up heads twice. What can you conclude from this experiment? Not much, because it's not that uncommon to get two heads with two tosses. In fact, the laws of probability say this should happen 25 percent of the time.

Next you toss the coin ten times

> **DO IT**
> **Flipping Coins**
> Take ten coins, shake them up, toss them, and note how many heads you get. Do this at least ten times. What's the most number of heads you got in a toss? What's the least number? How often did you get exactly five heads?

(or simultaneously toss ten identical coins). This time you get eight heads. Are the coins biased? Again, it is too soon to say. Seeing eight out of ten come up heads may make you suspicious, but you know that even for fair coins this can happen occasionally. This time probability theory tells us that you'll get eight or more heads about 5 percent of the time with unbiased coins. At this point you could say that you have a strong suspicion that the coins are biased, but that you need to do more tests.

Next suppose you toss the coin a hundred times (or toss 100 identical coins). If you get somewhere in the range of 45 to 55 heads, you'd conclude that the initial test was just one of those statistical fluctuations. But if you got 80 heads, you could be pretty certain that the coins are biased, for probability theory says the odds of getting 80 or more heads out of a 100 tosses are only slightly more than one chance in 2 billion. That would be some coincidence! You can see, then, how increasing the sample size increases our confidence in our conclusions (see Figure 4-2).

Sample size has been a problem with EMF studies. Childhood leukemia, for example, is relatively rare. According to the American Cancer Society, there were 2,600 new cases nationwide in 1992. By the time you narrow a study down to a single city, the number of cases is pretty small, even if you combine several years of data. Or consider the case of a California school whose teachers noticed an unusually high cancer rate among the staff. The school happened to be near some high-voltage power lines, and EMF readings were high. Is there a connection? According to the California epidemiologist Raymond Neutra, the state has 1,000 schools near such power lines, and the laws of probability indicate that at least ten out of any 1,000 schools should have unusually high cancer rates. The fact that this one school had a high cancer rate could be a statistical fluctuation, and the proximity of the power lines could be a coincidence. However, this observation doesn't mean that the original school should have no concern, for it's also possible that there is a real cause-and-effect relationship. One case simply doesn't give us enough information to make a reliable judgment. What's needed is a study comparing cancer rates in the 1,000 schools near power lines with rates in the 1,000 schools not near power lines, but so far no such study has been made. Even if such a study failed to find a statistical connection, that doesn't rule out the possibility that there was a special circumstance about the original school that did increase risks.

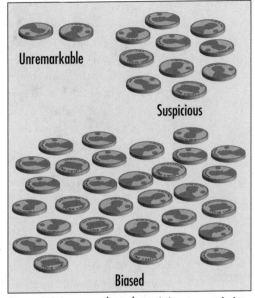

Figure 4-2 Large samples make statistics more convincing

In short, using statistical studies to demonstrate a connection between, say, a form of behavior and cancer is not an easy process. It can take a long time and a lot of thinking to determine what really is going on. What some feel to be compelling statistical evidence can be dismissed by others as inadequate.

LOOKING FOR CAUSE AND EFFECT

The most convincing way to demonstrate a connection is to determine actual cause and effect. For instance, the cause-and-effect relationship between falling from high places and broken bones is obvious. The physical effect of intense radioactivity on cells of the body is clear. Much less clear is the exact mechanism by which tobacco smoke can cause cancerous cells to develop. We probably won't understand that mechanism until we gain a fuller understanding of cancer, perhaps even including how to cure it.

Scientists are taking both approaches (statistics and looking for mechanisms) in evaluating the risks of EMFs.

They've come up with several interesting findings, which we'll discuss in Chapter 5.

Interpreting Risk

How small must a risk be before it's considered acceptable? Some would say only a zero risk is acceptable, but often that is not possible. There really is no cut-and-dried answer to this question, for different people have different tolerances for risk. Even one person may accept different risks in different circumstances. For instance, suppose you have the option of crossing the rapids via a narrow, slippery log. The presence of an irate bison on your side of the rapids could influence your judgment as to whether the risk of using the log is acceptable or not (see Figure 4-3). Or you might accept a risk that you would not subject a child to.

Let's look at some ways to evaluate risk data. Consider, for instance, the automobile accident death rate of 175 per million people. One way of interpreting this information is to ask what the average life expectancy would be if automobile accidents were the sole cause of death. That is, suppose you and every one else were immune to cancer, old age, terrorist bombs, falling anvils, and the like, but that you were still susceptible to automobile accidents. How long could you expect to live? The answer, assuming the accidental death rate doesn't change, is 3,960 years. Column 3 of Table 4-1 shows results for a range of death rates.

Another way of expressing the same information is calculating the number of years a particular risk would shorten a lifespan, on the average, assuming that you would live to be 100 otherwise. Column 4 in Table 4-1 shows the result of this calculation. For example, if cardiovascular disease were the only cause of death other than old age, it would cut your life span from 100 years down to 66 years.

These ways of viewing matters can help you interpret the importance of different risk factors. For instance, the risks of cardiovascular disease and of cancer appreciably affect the human lifespan. Reducing or eliminating these risks would have a noticeable effect on life expectancy.

Figure 4-3 Risk is subjective

PROCESS	DEATH RATE PER MILLION	AVERAGE LIFESPAN IN YEARS	LIFESPAN REDUCTION FROM 100 YEARS
cardiovascular disease	3573	194	34 years
cancer	2040	340	23 years
all accidents	353	1,960	4.9 years
auto accidents	175	3,960	2.5 years
falls	48	14,400	8 months
childhood leukemia	12	58,000	2 months
lightning	0.5	1,400,000	3 days

Table 4.1 Ways of looking at risk

Notice the entry for leukemia. The risk of contracting childhood leukemia is about 40 cases per million children per year, roughly the risk for dying in a fall. Fortunately the remission and recovery rate for childhood leukemia has risen from 4 percent to over 70 percent, so the death rate is closer to 12 per million.

Perception

The 1989 death rate per 100 million passenger miles is 1.12 for automobiles, 0.06 for railroads, and a mere 0.04 for scheduled airlines. Yet many more people are apprehensive about flying than about driving. One reason is that people don't react to risk merely by looking at the odds. They also look at how much control the individual has. As a car driver, you can tell yourself that your personal skills and safety habits make the risk much lower for yourself than for the public at large. In a threatening situation, you have the opportunity to react and save yourself. If you are a plane passenger, however, you are helpless and at the mercy of the actions of others. This has the psychological effect of magnifying one's perception of risk.

This difference in perception of risk really is quite misleading. Although most drivers perceive themselves as better than average, few drivers are *thirty times* safer than the average, the value that would be needed to reduce the risk level of driving to that of flying. People who indulge in high-risk activities often perceive those activities more as tests of competence than as risks. The sense of being in control moderates the sense of being at risk.

Another element that strongly influences our perception of risk is whether or not that risk if voluntary. For instance, suppose someone tells you that a nuclear power plant in your neighborhood would pose less risk than riding a bicycle. Most people, even if they accepted that claim, would feel much more uncomfortable about the nuclear plant than about riding a bicycle. One reason is you can choose whether or not to take the risk of riding a bicycle, but once the nuclear plant is in place, you don't have a choice about accepting its risk. For the same reason, people feel more uncomfortable about power lines generating EMFs than they do about other risks that are statistically greater.

Yet another important fact is avoidability. People are more likely to accept risks that seem unavoidable or which accompany an activity essential to them. A carpenter accepts the risks of working with power tools. A nurse accepts the risk of infection.

EMF risks strike most people as being involuntary and avoidable. That is, most people haven't had a say in the placement of power lines, and most feel the risk of power lines could have been avoided by situating them differently or by using a different technology. Furthermore, the risk seems greatest for children. All these factors make people react more strongly to the perceived risk of EMFs than they do to, say, the risks of accidents in the home.

EMF Research

How do we go about establishing whether or not EMFs are a health risk? A complete case for the assertion that EMFs are a health risk would demonstrate three things:

- A statistical connection between exposure to EMFs and the incidence of a disease

- An EMF-influenced biological process that produces or promotes the disease

- A specific mechanism by which EMFs could affect the biological process

The difference between the second and third points is the difference between seeing something happen and understanding why it happens. For instance, an example of the second point would be observing that exposing cancer cells to EMFs causes them to grow faster. An example of the third point would be discover-

QUICK LOOK

Researchers have investigated EMFs on several levels. Epidemiological studies have looked for statistical connections between residential EMF exposures and cancer and between occupational exposures to EMFs and cancer. Although there are questions about the validity of many of these studies, there is a persistent association of EMF exposure with childhood leukemia. Links to other forms of cancer are weaker or nonexistent.

Laboratory experiments with animals and living cells demonstrate that EMFs can have biological effects. Some experiments suggest that EMFs don't initiate cancer, but that they may promote existing cancers. Also, there is some evidence that EMFs may hinder the body's immune system. However, the evidence is neither comprehensive nor conclusive.

ing what precisely EMFs do to the cancer cells to make them grow faster.

Research has been going on for two decades in these areas, but the results are mixed and contradictory. It's a bit like working on a large jigsaw puzzle, in which it may turn out that not all the pieces are part of the same puzzle.

From the standpoint of public policy, sufficiently strong evidence of a statistical connection is enough to put us on the alert. Many of our current health recommendations, such as avoiding smoking and high-fat diets, stem initially from statistical studies. But research at the level of living cells is vital for developing an understanding of what's going on. Such an understanding, for example, could make clear which precautions are effective and which aren't. This is particularly important for EMFs because some evidence suggests that factors other than just the strength of EMFs are important in determining effects.

EMFs and Cancer: The Research

Current research concentrates on examining possible links between EMFs and cancer. That's because cancer is the only health risk that has been suggested by studies. In particular, the strongest evidence of an EMF health risk has been for a link between EMFs and childhood cancer. Most studies in the field fall into one of the three following categories:

1. *Epidemiological* studies: these are statistical studies that do things like comparing the cancer rates among people who live in high EMF areas to the rates among people living in low EMF areas.

2. Animal (*in vivo*) studies: these study the effects of EMFs on living animals, for example, studying the effect of high EMFs on mouse behavior. Animal studies have looked into a variety of possible effects, not just cancer. That's because the initial question scientists addressed is, "Is it possible for EMFs to have *any* effect on living systems?"

3. *In vitro* studies: these investigate the effects of EMFs on isolated tissues and cells, for example, studying the effect of EMFs on electrical activity near cell membranes.

Let's look at these studies in detail.

STATISTICAL STUDIES

In 1974 epidemiologist Dr. Nancy Wertheimer began looking for a link between childhood leukemia deaths in Denver and environmental factors. (An epidemiologist studies epidemic diseases, often by using statistical methods to connect a disease to other factors.) She obtained the addresses of childhood leukemia victims over a 20-year period in the Denver area, and she visited the sites, checking to see if there was any obvious clustering of sites that might point to environmental involvement.

She didn't find any clustering of sites, but she noticed that many of the homes of victims were close to power poles with transformers (electrical devices that convert electric power from one voltage to another). After seeing a magazine article suggesting EMFs were a hazard, she and physicist Ed Leeper came up with a way to estimate exposure to EMFs by looking at the proximity of houses to power poles and by classifying the power poles according to the amount of electric current they handled. This classification scheme became known as a *wiring configuration* or a *wiring code*, and has been used in many subsequent studies. In a paper published in 1979, Wertheimer and Leeper concluded that children living in homes with high-exposure wiring codes were two to three times as likely to die of leukemia as children living in homes with low-exposure wiring codes. (Appendix A contains more complete references for this and other scientific papers mentioned throughout this chapter.)

The Wertheimer-Leeper paper is a landmark, for it provided the first statistical link between EMFs and cancer. It also provoked a lot of controversy. Critics pointed out that the study merely estimated EMF exposure with wiring codes rather than monitoring the actual fields in the homes.

It didn't look into in-house sources of EMFs. The statistics were weak. There may have been confounding factors, as discussed in Chapter 4. The electric power industry dismissed the report as flawed. However, although many were skeptical of the Wertheimer-Leeper study, the results were too important to be left unchecked.

More Studies

The next three studies didn't clarify matters. One U.S. case study (by J. Fulton in 1980) and one British case study (by A. Myers in 1985) found no cancer-EMF link, while one Swedish study (by L. Tominius in 1986) did find an effect similar to the Wertheimer-Leeper study. However, none of these studies were rigorous, large, or complete enough to command attention.

The picture changed in 1988. At the request of the New York State Power Authority, Dr. David Savitz (then at the University of Colorado) and his colleagues undertook to replicate the Wertheimer-Leeper study. They studied data from the same geographical area (greater Denver), but used a different selection of leukemia victims, a more rigorous methodology, and more careful consideration of confounding factors. Their paper, published in 1988, also found an association between childhood cancer and high-exposure wiring codes. However, whereas Wertheimer found the risk to be increased by a factor of 2 to 3, Savitz found the risk increased by a factor of 1.5. Nonetheless, the Savitz study overcame many of the objections to the earlier Wertheimer study.

Later John Peters conducted a similar but more extensive study in Los Angeles. His studies included measuring magnetic fields at each home for at least 24 hours and interviewing the residents about electrical devices used by the children. He found the cancer rate at homes with measured high exposures to be about 1.5 times the normal rate. He found that homes with high-exposure wiring codes had cancer rates 2.5 times the normal. This raises a puzzling point that we'll return to later. Peters's 1991 report concluded that the data provided "little support for the relationship between magnetic field exposure and leukemia risk, some support for a relationship between wiring configuration and leukemia risk, and considerable support for a relationship between children's electrical appliance use and leukemia risks." The particular appliances singled out by the report are electric hair dryers and black-and-white televisions.

The largest and most recent study is the 1992 paper by Andres Ahlbom and Maria Feychting, examining the relationships between cancer and long-term exposures to EMFs in Sweden. They concluded that living near power lines increases the risk of childhood leukemia, with the increase in risk depending on the strength of the EMFs. An exposure to average fields of at least 1 mG doubled the risk, and an exposure to at least 4 mG increased the risk by four times. Also, there is a smaller increase in risk for adults. The study was based on 25 years of medical records for a half-million people.

Wiring Codes Vs. Magnetic Field Measurements

Several of the studies we've mentioned used wiring codes as a rough and quick way to estimate actual exposures to EMFs. One important question to settle is how reliably wiring codes do predict actual exposures. Wertheimer and Leeper, in two separate papers, compared magnetic measurements with their wiring codes and found that high-exposure wiring codes did, *on the average*, correspond to high magnetic field measurements. But the correspondence isn't exact. That is, the wiring codes for some houses don't predict the measured field strengths. One would expect, then, that a study based on actual field measurements would show a stronger connection with cancer than would a study based on the less-accurate wiring codes.

However, Peters found the opposite effect: wiring codes were more strongly associated with childhood cancer than were actual magnetic field measurements! This has a very important implication: if EMFs do cause cancer, it's not simply the strength of the field that matters. There must be one or more additional factors. What might these factors be? That's where animal and *in vitro* studies come in. They let researchers investigate the biological effects of magnetism more directly.

One possible factor is the relationship between the EMF and the natural geomagnetic field. Laboratory research suggests that some biological effects depend on the interaction between the EMF and the geomagnetic field. Peters and Joseph Bowman reanalyzed the Los Angeles data, this time comparing cancer rates with measurements that combined the geomagnetic field with the 60-Hz magnetic fields, and preliminary results show a much stronger connection with cancer rates. Certain combinations of geomagnetic field and 60-Hz field produced cancer rates six to nine times the normal rate, while other combinations had much lower, if any, risk.

INFO BOX
What to Measure
What does this uncertainty about what's important about EMFs mean to you? Currently, your only option for evaluating EMF risks in your home is to measure (or have measured) the EMF levels at various locations in and around your house. This may turn out to be a poor method for determining true risks. Until we learn more, however, EMF strength measurements are the only thing we have to work with.

If this finding holds up, it has some important consequences. First, simply measuring the strength of EMFs isn't enough to identify the real risk factor. Second, results reporting, say, that EMFs double the risk factor are lumping together people essentially at no extra risk with people with highly increased risk. Third, the key to minimizing EMF risks may be something other than just reducing exposure to EMFs.

These new results point out an important truth: without knowing the mechanisms by which EMFs can affect living organisms, we don't even know exactly what we should be measuring when looking for statistical risks. This is where laboratory work must fill in the missing details.

OCCUPATIONAL STUDIES

The statistical studies we've mentioned so far are residential studies, that is, studies that evaluate exposures to EMFs by examining where people live. Another statistical approach is to look at occupations that are subjected to high EMF levels. For the most part, these studies have assumed certain occupations, such as power station operators, telephone linemen, and telegraph operators, have enhanced exposures to EMFs without making systematic measurements to determine the exposures. Many of these studies do indicate an elevated risk for leukemia. Some also suggest that electrical workers are at increased risk for brain tumors.

Probably the most definitive study to date is Dr. Genevieve Matanoski's study of 50,000 active male telephone company employees. She found a higher risk for leukemia in general. The subgroup with the highest exposures —cable splicers— also had the greatest increase in risk for cancers of all kinds. On the other hand, a recent study conducted by UCLA and Southern California Edison of 36,000 Edison employees with on-the-job EMF exposure showed that those with the highest exposures did not have an unusually high cancer rate.

 IN DEPTH
Ionizing Radiation
Radiation that produces fields powerful enough to rip electrons off atoms and to break molecular bonds is termed *ionizing radiation*. Such radiation can have direct biological effects, such as damaging a cell or altering a DNA molecule. The frequency of the radiation determines if it is ionizing or not. If the frequency is not high enough, even enormous amounts of radiation will not be ionizing. The threshold frequency for ionizing radiation occurs in the ultraviolet band. Lower frequencies are safe, at least as far as ionization goes. Waves associated with 60-Hz EMFs fall far short (by a factor of 50 trillion!) of the threshold frequency. Thus scientists seek subtle, indirect mechanisms when trying to see how 60-Hz EMFs can have biological effects.

These studies aren't really directly comparable to residential studies. For instance, some electrical workers are subjected to much higher levels of EMFs than you would find in the home. It could be that very high levels of EMFs produce effects that don't occur at lower levels. Also, electrical workers may be exposed to additional potential hazards, such as VLF radiation, microwaves, and chemicals used in the industry. From the standpoint of the electrical worker, the exact cause is less important than being at an increased risk. From the standpoint of someone concerned with residential risks, it's not clear to what extent occupational risks imply a residential risk. From the scientific standpoint, as usual in this field, more research is needed.

ANIMAL AND *IN VITRO* STUDIES

In the 1970s most scientists felt the magnetic fields were too small to have any effect at all, let alone to cause cancer. Therefore much of the work in animal and *in vitro* studies has been directed to the broader question of whether EMFs can have *any* biological effect *(bioeffect,* for short).

Certainly some forms of electromagnetic waves, such as X-rays and ultraviolet, can cause bioeffects, including cancer, but the fields associated with these waves are much more energetic than 60-Hz EMFs. X-rays and ultraviolet are examples of ionizing radiation. The prevailing view had been that only ionizing radiation could produce bioeffects. However, the current evidence indicates that EMFs can also produce bioeffects.

EMFs and Bioeffects

Several experiments in the last two or three decades indicate that low-frequency electromagnetic fields can have biological effects. Do these effects include cancer? Many studies show no such effect, while others do suggest a connection. The situation is complex. For instance, a test that finds that EMFs don't increase abnormal pregnancies in mice doesn't say anything about the relationship between human leukemia and EMFs. A test that shows that a strong magnetic field changing once a minute affects hormone production in rats doesn't necessarily indicate what a weaker field fluctuating 60 times a second does to hormone production in humans. Let's examine some studies.

Some experiments that haven't used 60-Hz EMFs are nonetheless suggestive. Ross Adey, S.M. Bawin and colleagues at the Brain Research Institute at UCLA looked for biological effects from microwaves, which have much higher frequencies. However, rather than using continuous microwaves, they sent pulses of microwaves, varying the pulse rate. Pulse rates in the ELF range, including 60 Hz, seemed particularly effective in doing things such as affecting brain waves in cats and monkeys and altering calcium levels in

INFO BOX
Cancer Initiation,
Promotion, and
Prevention

Many cancer researchers feel that cancer develops in stages. The first stage, initiation, occurs when some agent (called an *initiator*) modifies DNA in a way that makes it susceptible to the next stage. The next stage, promotion, occurs when another agent (called a *promoter*) stimulates an initiated cell into rapid growth. The third stage, progression, is when the growth becomes malignant. This stage may be assisted by a third class of agents. The agents that aid progression may differ from the agents that aid promotion, and both may be different from the agents that act as initiators.

chick brains. This suggests that living things are sensitive to these particular frequencies.

Since the 1950s doctors have used bone growth stimulators to accelerate the healing of broken bones. These stimulators use 72-Hz electric currents, which, in an unknown fashion, speed up *mitosis,* or cell division. While accelerated cell division is good for bones, it also is a feature of cancerous growth. Several researchers have followed up on this idea. They exposed cancer cells to EMFs (*in vitro* studies), and found that EMFs accelerate the growth of cancer cells. These results indicate that EMFs may be a cancer promoter rather than a cancer initiator. That is, the presence of EMFs may promote an existing cancer that otherwise would have been overcome by the body's natural defenses. (See the box on initiation, promotion, and progression.)

A 1968 paper by Jerry Phillips and Wendell Winters is an example of research suggesting that EMFs may assist the progression stage in cancer. They took cancer cells that had already gone through initiation and promotion, and subjected some to EMFs and left others alone. The cancer cells subjected to the EMFs grew faster than the control group. On the other hand, studies to date have failed to find any genetic changes in cells exposed to EMFs, which suggests that EMFs are not a cancer initiator.

Another line of experiments suggests that exposures to EMFs may suppress the production of the hormone melatonin. Normally darkness triggers the production of melatonin, which helps regulate the body's day-night rhythms. Altering the production of melatonin may cause sleep disorders, mood changes, fatigue, deficient immune responses, and increased cancer risk. These all are effects that seem to have occurred in at least some animal-EMF experiments. Possibly the magnetic fields affect the retina in the eye in the same fashion that light does, triggering the cut-off of melatonin production. Russel Reiter of the University of Texas reported the suppression of melatonin in rats in 1988. However, his experiments switched 200 mG DC to 400 mG DC (nonoscillating magnetic fields) back and forth at the rate of once a minute for an hour, so they don't closely resemble real-life conditions. Also, the link between melatonin and the immune system isn't firmly established.

Note that experiments suggest at least two ways in which EMFs might be linked with cancer:

1. EMFs may promote the development of existing cancers.

2. EMFs may suppress melatonin production, which, in turn may weaken the body's immune system response to cancer.

These results don't prove EMFs cause or promote cancer. They do begin to make it plausible that such connections could exist, and they point the way to further research.

Mechanisms?

Many experiments have attempted to determine what observable effects, if any, EMFs have on life. At this point it is clear that EMFs do have some effects. A more basic question is, what is the mechanism? How is it that EMFs can affect living matter?

Researchers have made some progress with this question. For example, some experiments subjecting cancer cells to EMFs suggested that EMFs could weaken the immune system response. That observation by itself doesn't help us understand what is happening. The melatonin research mentioned above, however, takes matters a step further by suggesting that the mechanism for weakening the immune system is suppressing melatonin production. The next step is to discover the mechanism that allows EMFs to suppress melatonin production. As mentioned, it's been suggested that EMFs affect the retina the same way that light does when light acts to suppress production. This last supposition remains to be demonstrated. If you can trace an apparent relationship between a bioeffect and EMFs down to a specific mechanism, you've made a much stronger case for the relationship and you've greatly improved our understanding of what's going on.

Some experiments suggest that changing field strengths are more important than the field strengths themselves. That is, moving in and out of, say, a 50-mG 60-Hz field may have more biological effects than simply staying in the field. Researchers are just beginning to look into the effects of *transient fields*— EMFs that vary in strength, perhaps rapidly, and EMFs that are intermittent in nature. It could turn out that measuring such variations may be more important than measuring the average field strength, if you wish to evaluate risks.

Peters and Bowman found that combined measurements of EMFs and the geomagnetic field may be a better predictor of cancer risk than EMF measurements alone. They were guided by laboratory tests that suggest that certain values for the geomagnetic field resonate with (reinforce in some way) the 60-Hz EMFs. Resonance can greatly amplify the effect of an oscillation. If resonance occurs, then simple EMF measurements tell only part of the story. (Chapter 6 describes this in more detail.)

The most convincing evidence that EMFs were dangerous would be to find a specific mechanism by which EMFs could adversely affect

> **INFO BOX**
> **Hair Dryers**
> One of the strongest correlations the 1991 Peters' paper found was between the use of hair dryers and childhood leukemia. Although hair dryers do generate high EMFs, they are used only for short periods of time. But because the use of a hair dryer involves moving it around, it does expose the user to varying field strengths. Thus this case study result is consistent with the idea that changing magnetic fields may be more harmful than ones of constant strength.

a living cell. Here scientists currently are examining some possibilities. The problem, as you saw, is that EMFs carry too little energy to do much. One possibility is that EMFs may interact with living cells on the information level rather than in terms of energy. Consider this analogy. The energy carried by radio waves or television waves is small, and these waves have no direct effect on you. But the information they carry can make you laugh, groan, or even rush to your storm cellar.

What does this have to do with EMFs? First, the cells of the human body use a variety of complex electromagnetic processes. For instance, many cellular activities involve the transport of molecules and ions across membranes. This process involves the electrical properties of the membranes, the molecules, and the ions and conceivably could be influenced by EMFs. Nerve impulses are an electrochemical activity. The complex reactions involved in duplicating DNA and producing proteins have an electrochemical component. In essence, these electrical activities are part of the information system that controls the processes in a living cell.

Second, one important feature of oscillating magnetic fields, such as EMFs, is that they generate voltages. In living cells, which are conductors of electricity, these voltages will produce small electric currents that could mimic or interfere with the normal electrical activities that take place in cells. That is, they could interfere with the natural information flow in a cell, thus altering some processes. Steady fields, like the geomagnetic field, don't generate voltages. This is why it is plausible that 60-Hz EMFs can produce biological effects even though their magnetic fields typically are much weaker than the geomagnetic field.

The Bottom Line

Many questions remain about the bioeffects of EMFs. For example, what is the effect of frequency? Would, say, a 200-Hz frequency have greater or lesser effects than 50 Hz? How do bioeffects depend on the combination of duration of exposure and the strengths of fields? For instance, does one day's exposure to 100 mG have the same effect as a 100 days' exposure to 1 mG? If high EMFs are a health threat, what's a safe level? Is the orientation of the field relative to the Earth's field important? How well do rat studies carry over to humans? At the atomic and molecular level, how do EMFs cause bioeffects? Is an EMF-cancer link the only health concern about EMFs? How important are transient effects? In short, there is a lot of work to be done before we can understand the relationship between EMFs and the human body.

Statistical studies of residential and occupational data yield a mixture of results. Individual studies often have statistical and methodological weaknesses. Nonetheless, there is a persistent pattern linking EMFs to increased risk of childhood leukemia, a pattern confirmed by the best and most complete case studies to date. EMFs in excess of 2 mG or so seem to increase the risk by factors ranging from about 1.5 to 4, depending on the study. Possible connections to other effects, such as adult leukemia and brain cancer, have much weaker support.

Some evidence suggests, however, that average EMF strength alone may not be the best predictor of risk. Certain combinations of EMFs and the Earth's magnetic field may be significantly more harmful than others.

Laboratory experiments verify that EMFs can have biological effects but are tentative about connections to cancer. Some evidence suggests that EMFs may promote existing cancers but not initiate cancer. Other evidence suggests that EMFs may interfere with the immune system.

In short, present evidence makes an EMF-cancer link plausible, but not certain.

EMFs Up Close and Personal

6

EMFs are electromagnetic fields produced by moving electric charges. If that's enough to satisfy you, read no further! But if you do want to know more about what really goes on, this chapter is for you.

First, let's provide some background. The history of electricity and magnetism goes back to classic Greek and Chinese civilizations, but scientists didn't recognize that the two (electricity and magnetism) were related until the nineteenth century. We'll follow that historical perspective by looking at electricity and magnetism separately before tackling electromagnetism.

Electricity

Over 2,500 years ago, the Greeks discovered that rubbing amber briskly against fur endowed the amber with an unusual property: it would attract small bits of matter, such as feathers and bits of straw. At

QUICK LOOK
Electric charge is a basic property of atomic particles. Electrons carry a negative charge and protons have a positive charge. An atom or molecule normally has equal numbers of electrons and protons and so has no total charge. By adding or removing electrons from an atom or a molecule, you can turn it into a negative or positive charge. An electric charge produces an electric field, which then can affect other charges.

Moving charges are an electric current, and an electric current generates a magnetic field. An AC (alternating current) circuit, in which the current flows first one direction, then the other, produces a fluctuating magnetic field. A fluctuating magnetic field produces a fluctuating electric field, a fluctuating

continued on next page

the time it seemed to be a mildly interesting phenomenon of minor importance.

Eventually it became apparent that there are two kinds of electricity—*positive* and *negative*. An object with negative electricity is said to be *negatively charged*, and an object with positive electricity is said to be *positively charged*. Two bodies with the same kind of charge repel each other, and two bodies with opposite charges attract each other. Experimenters determined that ordinary, uncharged bodies really hold equal amounts of positive and negative charge. When you rub, say, amber with wool, you transfer some negative charge from the wool to the amber. This gives the amber more negative charges than positive charges, so the amber becomes negatively charged. The wool, on the other hand, now has a deficit of negative charges, leaving it positively charged. See Figure 6-1. A modern way to get the same effect is to rub your hair or a wool sweater with an inflated rubber balloon.

> **QUICK LOOK**
> *continued from previous page*
>
> electric field produces a fluctuating magnetic field, and so on. This process generates electromagnetic waves, that is, waves made of fluctuating electric fields and magnetic fields. These fields then propagate through space. Our electric power system produces 60-Hz currents, meaning currents oscillate 60 times a second. These currents generate 60-Hz electromagnetic waves, know as EMF waves, ELF waves, or power frequency waves. The electric component of these waves doesn't penetrate our bodies, but the magnetic field does.
>
> The energy in EMF radiation is much too small to directly damage anything in a living cell. However, an oscillating magnetic field in our body will generate small voltages which can produce small electric currents in our body cells and which might interfere with or enhance natural bioelectrical processes.

ELECTRIC CHARGES AND ATOMS

Electric charge is an extremely basic property of matter, for the particles from which atoms are made carry electric charges. As you probably know, atoms are constructed from three kinds of particles: electrons, protons, and neutrons. An electron has a negative charge, and every electron has exactly the same amount of

> **INFO BOX**
> **Names**
> We get our name for electricity from the Greek word for amber, which was elektron.

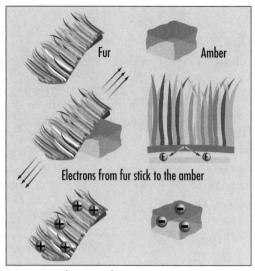

Figure 6-1 Charging amber

charge as every other electron. Physicists call this basic amount of charge -e, with the minus sign indicating a negative charge. Every proton also has exactly the same charge, except the charge is positive, or +e. Neutrons are neutral. (Actually physicists who shot high-energy beams of electrons at neutrons found that neutrons do contain positive and negative charges within them, but in equal amounts. Modern particle theory attributes the charge to *quarks,* particles from which protons and neutrons are made.) Ordinarily an atom has equal numbers of protons and electrons so that the net charge is zero.

If you remove an electron from an atom, it has a net positive charge and is called a *positive ion* (see Figure 6-2). If you add an extra electron to an atom, the atom has a net negative charge and is called a *negative ion.*

To charge a body electrically, we have to get some atoms to shed their electrons. That's what happens when you rub amber with fur or rubber with wool. Electrons get dislodged from molecules in the fur or wool and transfer to the amber or rubber, where they attach

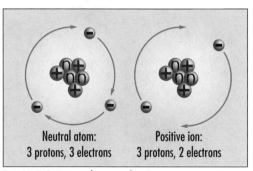

Figure 6-2 A neutral atom and an ion

loosely to the molecules there.

STATIC ELECTRICITY

Static electricity refers to situations in which objects have an electric charge; *static* means that the charges stay put. In other words we aren't talking about moving charges, just stationary charges. Stationary charges attract or repel each other, depending on whether they have unlike or like charges. A large enough static charge can cause a spark to jump between positively and negatively charged objects. For example, sliding across some car seats can give you a static charge that gets discharged by a spark when you reach for the metal door handle. The French physicist Charles-Augustin de Coulomb investigated the forces between static charges and discovered that this electric force, like gravity, was an inverse square force. That means increasing the distance by, say, a factor of ten decreases the force (that's the inverse part) by a factor of ten squared, or one hundred (that's the square part).

> **DO IT**
> **Static Electricity**
> Take an inflated rubber balloon and rub it vigorously with something furlike, such as your head, a sweater, a cat. Place the balloon up against a wall. If nature isn't being particularly perverse, the balloon will stick to the wall. What's happened is this. Rubbing the balloon against the fur causes the balloon to pick up some extra electrons, charging it negatively. As you place the balloon near the wall, the balloon's negative charge repels some of the electrons in the wall away from their usual places, leaving a surplus of positive charge behind. These positive charges attract the negatively charged balloon, holding it in place (see Figure 6-3).

Magnetism

Now let's jump back

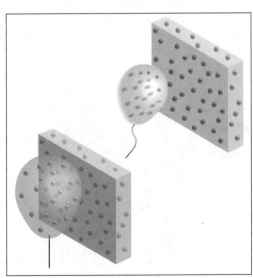

Figure 6-3 Balloon with static electricity attracted to a wall

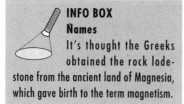

INFO BOX
Names
It's thought the Greeks obtained the rock lodestone from the ancient land of Magnesia, which gave birth to the term magnetism.

in time and look at magnetism. Greek philosophers had observed that a certain kind of rock called a lodestone had the ability to attract iron.

Magnetism seems similar to electricity in that both feature hunks of material that seem to be able to attract bits of matter, but the details are different. Charged amber attracts feathers, bits of straw, bits of paper, and the like, and you have to rub amber to charge it. Magnets only attract iron and related metals and alloys, such as steel and nickel. A magnet doesn't attract or repel electric charges, and an electric charge doesn't attract or repel magnets.

But there are other similarities, too. For instance, just as there are two kinds of electric charges, there are two magnetic polarities, which have been dubbed *north* and *south*. Like polarities repel each other, and unlike polarities attract each other, as you can verify by playing with magnets. However, there doesn't seem to be an exact analog to electric charges. That is, no one has ever found an isolated north charge or an isolated south charge. Instead north and south always come in pairs, as the two opposite poles of a magnet. If you cut a magnet in half, you don't isolate the north and south parts. Instead, (see Figure 6-4) you get two magnets, each with a north and south pole.

Electric and Magnetic Fields

What scientists observe and what you observe are the effects of electricity and magnetism: bodies being attracted to or repelled from one another.

Figure 6-4 Slicing a magnet produces two magnets

produce certain kinds of forces. Several scientists, mostly in the nineteenth century, worked out what these forces should be in order to produce the effects we see. To help visualize what's going on, physicists came up with the idea of the

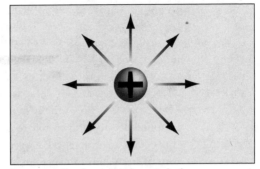

Figure 6-5 The electric field for a single charge

field. Instead of thinking of a charge as somehow pushing or pulling a second charge, think of each charge as producing a kind of invisible influence in the surrounding space. We call this influence an *electric field*. To find the strength of a force on a charged particle sitting in an electric field, you multiply the charge times the field. Thus strong fields produce a bigger effect on a charge than weak fields. You can draw fields produced by different arrangements of charges. The direction of the field at any particular location shows the direction of the force a positive charge would feel if placed there. The closeness of field lines to each other indicates the strength of the field, with close lines indicating strong forces. Figure 6-5 shows the electric field produced by a single positive charge. The field points away from the charge because that is the direction a positive charge would be pushed. The fact that the field lines are closer to each

other near the charge means the field is stronger there. The field for a negative charge would look the same, except it would point toward the charge instead of away. That's because a positive charge would be attracted.

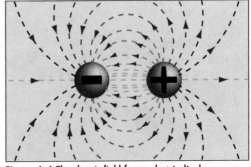

Figure 6-6 The electric field for an electric dipole.

Figure 6-7 A magnetic dipole field

Figure 6-6 shows the electric field created by two equal but oppositely charged particles. Physicists call this a *dipole* field. Dipole means two poles or two polarities, positive and negative. The field is quite weak far from the charges because the field of the negative charge tends to cancel the field from the positive charge. However, the field is strong in the regions between the two charges because there the fields from the two charges add together. The cancellation effect away from the paired charges is analogous to an EMF cancellation effect for paired electric currents, an effect you saw in Chapter 5.

Similarly a magnetic field shows the effect of magnetic poles. The direction of the field shows the direction of the force a magnetic north pole would feel. It also shows the direction a tiny magnet would point. The field would push the north end one way and pull the south end the opposite direction, lining up the magnet with the field. Figure 6-7 shows the magnetic field for a magnet. Magnets, by necessity, have two poles, so this is a magnetic dipole field.

So what's the difference between an electric field and a magnetic field? The electric field affects electric charges, and the magnetic field affects magnetic poles. A magnet attracts or repels magnetic poles, but it doesn't attract or repeal electric charges. Similarly electric charges attract or repeal other electric charges, but they don't attract or repel magnetic poles.

DO IT
Magnetic Fields
You can more or less "see" a magnetic field if you have access to a good magnet and iron filings. Sprinkle iron filings over a stiff piece of paper or cardboard, then bring a magnet up underneath the paper. The magnetic field will magnetize the iron filings, turning each filing into a small magnet. The filings then line up with the magnetic field, clustering where the field is strongest.

Electromagnetism

One of the exciting discoveries of nineteenth-century physics was that electricity and magnetism are related. A stationary electric charge produces just an electric field, but a moving electric charge also produces a magnetic field. For instance, an electric current flowing along a straight wire produces a magnetic field circling the wire (see Figure 6-8). If you make the current flow in a loop, you get a magnetic dipole field that looks a lot like the magnetic field produced by a magnet (see Figure 6-9).

Not only do moving charges produce magnetic fields, but magnetic fields affect moving charges. If you put a charged particle in a magnetic field and just let it sit there, it won't feel a force. If you set the charge in motion so that it moves parallel to the field, the charge won't feel a force. But if you try to move the charge at right angles to a magnetic field, the charge feels a force that is perpendicular to the magnetic field and perpendicular to the direction it's moving. Pushing sideways on a moving object changes the direction it's going, and that's what happens here. A magnetic field deflects a moving charge into a circular motion (see Figure 6-11.)

Suppose a charge is traveling not exactly at a right angle to the field and not exactly parallel to the field. In that case, the charge will wind up spiraling along the field lines (see Figure 6-12).

The Earth's magnetic field, for example, traps charged particles from the sun in this fashion. The trapped particles spiral back and forth in the Van Allen belts, magnetic fields high above our atmos-

**IN DEPTH
The Geomagnetic Field**

The Earth produces its own magnetic field, called the geomagnetic field. This is the field that causes compasses to point North (or South, depending upon your orientation). The strength of this field depends upon your location, but it typically is of the order of 0.5 G, or 500 mG. Figure 6-10 sketches the geomagnetic field. Geologists believe the field is generated by electric currents deep in the core of the Earth. (You might guess that the Earth's inner solid iron core was just a big magnet, but an iron magnet would lose its magnetism at the high temperatures found in the core.) Although we've described the geomagnetic field as being static, it does oscillate, but it does so irregularly and on a time scale of hundreds of thousands of years.

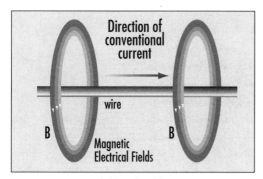

Figure 6-8 Magnetic field produced by a current in a straight wire

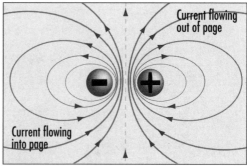

Figure 6-9 Magnetic field of a current loop

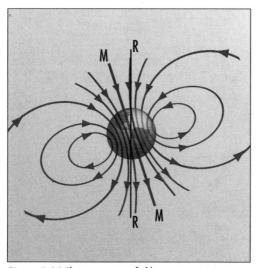

Figure 6-10 The geomagnetic field

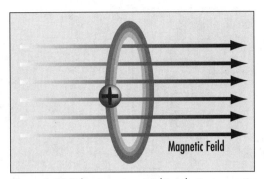

Figure 6-11 A charge moving at right angles to a magnetic field

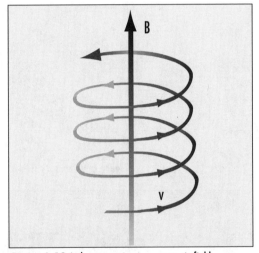

Figure 6-12 A charge moving in a magnetic field

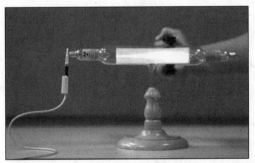

Figure 6-13 A magnet deflecting a beam of electrons

**IN THE LAB
Deflecting
Electrons**

If you hold a strong magnet against the side of a television (and we do *not* recommend you try this), you'll see that the picture distorts. That's because the picture is painted on the screen by a beam of electrons, and the magnetic field from the magnet deflects the beam. The problem is that the magnet may magnetize elements in the TV, leaving a permanent distortion. Figure 6-13 shows a simple set-up illustrating the same effect. Applying high voltage to the left end of the tube produces an electron beam made visible by a phosporescent strip in the tube. Bringing a magnet in bends the beam.

phere (see Figure 6-14). Some particles get channeled along the field lines to the North or South magnetic pole. When they hit the atmosphere, they ionize some of the gases, which then emit the light we call the Northern or Southern Lights.

Nature is often symmetrical. Just as moving charges can produce a magnetic field, moving magnets can generate an electric field. Indeed, from the standpoint of Einstein's theory of relativity, the distinction between the magnetic and electric fields becomes blurred. What one observer measures as an electric field might be measured as a magnetic field (and vice versa) by a second observer moving relative to the first.

But that digresses a bit. Let's return to the magnetic fields produced by currents, since that is what EMFs are about.

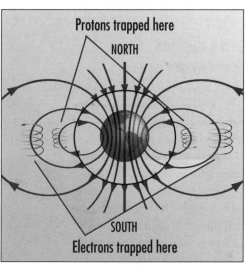

Figure 6-14 Charges trapped by the geomagnetic field

AC and DC Electric Currents

A current is a flow of electric charge. The flow can be just in one direction, in which case we call it direct current, or *DC.* Or the flow can alternate in the direction it flows, in which case we call it alternating current, or *AC.* In metal wiring the electrons carry the charge. Metals have the property that some of the electrons, instead of being attached to particular atoms, roam freely through the metal. In a conducting solution, such as salt water and the fluids in your body, positive and negative ions carry the current. The direction of a current is defined as the direction a positive charge would flow. Thus in a wire the current direc-

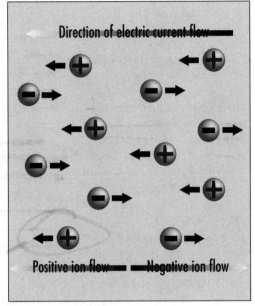

Figure 6-15 Current flow

tion is opposite the direction the electrons move. In a conducting solution, the positive ions move in the direction of the current, and the negative ions move in the opposite direction (see Figure 6-15).

DIRECT ELECTRIC CURRENTS

A battery produces a direct current. It acts like an electron pump, pushing electrons into one end of the circuit and retrieving them from the other. As they travel, the electrons lose energy as they overcome the resistance of moving through the wire, much as water loses energy when pushed through a long hose. The lost energy can appear as heat, which is the idea behind the electric heater and the electric stove. If the conducting wire gets hot enough, it will glow brightly, which is the idea behind the incandescent light bulb. in which the current is forced through a narrow filament, heating it to thousands of degrees. Note that running a current through a wire doesn't charge a wire, for as many electrons enter one end as leave the other. Any section of the wire has as many positive charges as negative charges. But the negative charges, at least some of them, are moving, and that motion produces a magnetic field. As long as the current doesn't change, the magnetic field doesn't change; it is a static magnetic field.

A battery's ability to push current through a circuit is measured by its voltage. You can think of voltage as being the electronic equivalent of pressure. Just as higher water pressure can push more water per second through a hose, a higher voltage pushes a greater current through a circuit. Current doesn't get used up. The current flowing into a light bulb equals the current flowing out. However, the electrons have lost energy. The situation is similar to using a stream of water to turn a water wheel. The amount of water flowing into the device equals the amount coming out, but the exiting water has lost energy.

> **INFO BOX**
> **Why AC?**
> Alternating current has a major advantage over direct current: with AC you can easily step up or step down the voltages with a transformer. Why is this a plus? When you transmit electricity over power lines, there always is some energy lost to the resistance in the power line. It turns out that increasing the voltage reduces the amount of power loss for transmitting a given amount of power. For this reason long-distance power transmission lines operate at voltages from 69,000 V to 750,000 V. However, most of us would feel a little uncomfortable if our household appliances operated at 750,000 V instead of 115 V. With AC power it's a simple matter to convert the high voltages to lower voltages. Typically this is done in two steps. The transmission voltages are stepped down to from 5,000 V to 35,000 V for short-range distribution, then down to 120 V to 240 V for neighborhood distribution.

ALTERNATING ELECTRIC CURRENTS

Our power system uses alternating current instead of direct current. Alternating currents are much more complex in their effects than direct currents. AC voltages typically are generated by some sort of rotating device, such as water-driven turbine or motor-driven generator. Consider connecting a light bulb to an AC source. First the current moves in one direction. Then the voltage and current drop to zero. Next, as voltage changes to the opposite sign, the current flows in the other direction. Once again, the voltage and current go to zero, then the cycle repeats. If human vision reacted fast enough, you'd see the light brighten and dim twice each full cycle (see Figure 6-16).

This back-and-forth motion may strike you as ineffectual, but many electrical devices depend only on the heat generated as the current is forced through. In this case all that matters is that there is a current. Whether it goes just one direction or sloshes back and forth isn't important. So AC current is fine for devices like light bulbs, toasters,

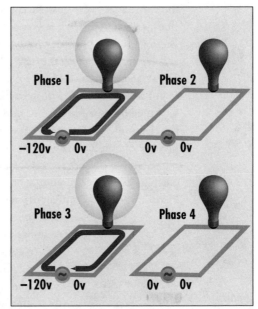

Figure 6-16 Alternating current flow

electric stoves, electric heaters, hair dryers, and the like. Other devices, like electric motors, don't depend on heating, but they can be designed to work off AC. Finally some types of electronic equipment do require DC, for example, a computer or parts of a television set. In these cases the equipment contains transformers to convert AC to DC.

AC Effects

A constant direct current produces a static magnetic field. An alternating current produces an alternating magnetic field, one that gets weaker and stronger and changes direction as the current gets weaker and stronger and changes direction. One of the more amazing discoveries of nineteenth-century physics was that a changing magnetic field produces a changing electric field. This is the idea behind the spinning turbines used to generate electricity.

Thus an alternating current produces both a magnetic field and an electric field, even though the circuit has no net charge. Furthermore, it turns out that a changing electric field produces a changing magnetic field. Let's repeat these two properties:

↳ A changing magnetic field produces a changing electric field

↳ A changing electric field produces a changing magnetic field.

It looks like once you get something like this started, it will perpetuate itself. That is, a changing magnetic field will produce a changing electric field that will produce a changing magnetic field that will produce a changing electric field, and so on, ad infinitum. And that's what happens! The result is an electromagnetic wave. Consider a television transmitter, for example. The transmitter produces an alternating current in the antenna. This generates alternating electric and magnetic fields that propagate through space, with the electric part sending a magnetic field forward, and the magnetic part sending an electric field forward. When the wave reaches your receiving antenna, the oscillating electric field pushes on the electrons in the antenna, producing a small alternating current, which then transmits the signal to your television.

Electrical transmission lines and the wiring in your house act just like the TV transmitting antenna. Each moves electrons back and forth along a wire. The main difference is that the TV signal oscillates hundreds of millions of times a second, while our electrical power system currents oscillate 60 times a second.

**IN THE LAB
Look Ma! No
Wires!**

The distinctive property of AC magnetic fields as compared to static (DC) magnetic fields, is that AC magnetic fields generate voltages, which can produce electric currents. Figure 6-17 shows a long coil plugged into a 120-V, 60-Hz circuit. The coil has an iron core to multiply the field strength. Above it you can see a coil of wire connected to a light bulb. The 60-Hz current produces a 60 Hz magnetic field, and the magnetic field produces a voltage in the wire coil connected to the light bulb. In Figure 6-17, the voltage and current are too weak to light the bulb. In Figure 6-18, however, the coil has been moved closer to the iron core. There the oscillating field is strong enough (about 200 gauss) to produce enough voltage and current to light the bulb. Note that 200 gauss is 200,000 mG, so this field is far stronger than the EMFs you might encounter in the home.

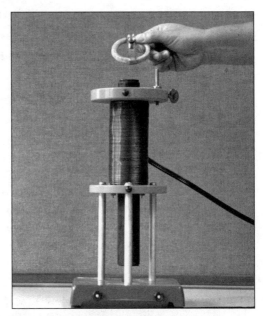

Figure 6-17 The coil and the light bulb

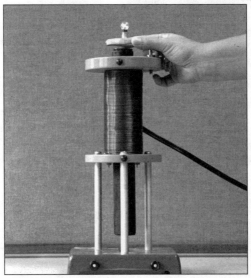

Figure 6-18 Changing magnetic fields from the coil produce a current to light the bulb

THE AC-DC INTERACTION

One recent development in EMF research is paying attention to possible interactions between EMFs, which are oscillating fields, and the geomagnetic field, which is static. As mentioned in Chapter 5, combined EMF and geomagnetic fields may be a better predictor of risk than EMF measurements alone. Researchers suspect a resonance effect.

IN DEPTH
Electromagnetic Waves

The electromagnetic fields produced by power lines propagate through space. They, along with light, radio waves, and several other kinds of waves are all variations of the same basic phenomenon, *the electromagnetic wave*. All electromagnetic waves travel at the speed of light and all are made up of oscillating electromagnetic fields. The only differences are in frequency and in wavelength, which is the distance a wave travels during one oscillation. The frequency and wavelength are related inversely, which means increasing the frequency decreases the wavelength. Figure 6-19 shows a snapshot of some waves being produced by electric currents. The more frequently the current oscillates, the shorter the wavelength. That makes sense, for a wave that oscillates quickly takes less time per cycle, so it travels a smaller distance each cycle. Sixty-Hz currents produce EMFs with wavelengths of about 3,100 miles. FM radio transmitters produce electromagnetic waves with wavelengths of about 10 feet.

Resonance occurs when an oscillation is reinforced by something else vibrating at the same rate. For example, suppose you're pushing on a tire hanging from a rope to get it swinging. You're most effective if you synchronize your pushes with the frequency at which the tire is swinging. Or if you sing in the shower, you'll find that certain notes seem amplified. That occurs when the notes you sing have the same frequency at which air in a container the size of your shower naturally vibrates. Or perhaps you've driven in a car with unbalanced tires and noticed that it vibrates at certain speeds. What's happening here is that a car has a natural frequency at which its springs tend to vibrate. The unbalanced tires give a little jolt to the car each tire revolution. At a certain speed, those jolts come at the same frequency the springs oscillate, and the car begins to vibrate. That's resonance. The important points about resonance are that it occurs when two frequencies match and that it magnifies effects.

Next let's look at how there can be a resonance effect between the geomagnetic fields and EMFs. Half of the equation seems present, for EMFs os-

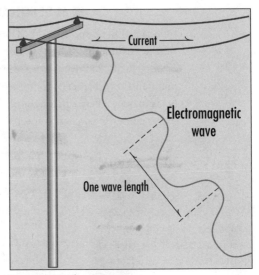

Figure 6-19 Electromagnetic waves.

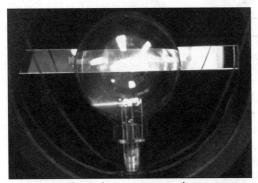

Figure 6-20 Electron beam in an argon tube

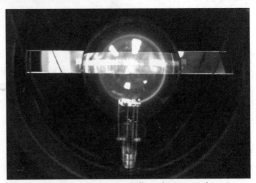

Figure 6-21 Electrons beam deflected into a circle

IN THE LAB
Magnetic Fields and
Changes in Motion

Figure 6-20 shows a beam of electrons. The beam itself is invisible, but it's produced in a tube containing the gas argon. As the beam blasts through the argon, it energizes the argon atoms, making them glow. So the glow marks the path of the electrons through the argon. The entire tube is inside a set of coils which can produce a static magnetic field of about 15 gauss (that's about 30 times the strength of the Earth's magnetic field) when an electric current flows along the coils. Figure 6-21 shows what happens when this magnetic field is turned on. The magnetic field deflects the electrons so that they flow in a circle instead of a straight line. The number of times the electrons flow around the circle per second is the cyclotron frequency. The whole set-up is a neat example of the connection between electricity and magnetism. Electric current flowing through the coils produces a magnetic field in the interior of the coils, and that magnetic field deflects moving electrons.

cillate. But where does resonance come in? After all, the geomagnetic field doesn't oscillate. That answer lies in the effect the geomagnetic field has on currents in the body. First, keep in mind that the body naturally produces small electrical currents. Some, such as nerve impulses in the brain and the heart, are strong enough to be picked up by devices designed to monitor the brain and heart. Other currents are exceedingly small and occur within a cell as various processes take place. These currents are part of the process of living. Second, remember the effect a magnetic field has on moving charges: it deflects them into circular or helical paths. The charges will circle around the magnetic field with a frequency that depends on the mass of a charge, the size of its electric charge, and the strength of the magnetic field. This frequency is called the *cyclotron frequency,* for the cyclotron was based on the concept of a magnetic field forcing charged particles to move in a circle. For certain ions and certain strengths of the geomagnetic field, this cyclotron frequency matches the 60-Hz frequency of EMFs, and this is where resonance could take place. For the strongest effect, the AC magnetic field should be parallel to the geomagnetic field. As to what the effect of that resonance would be, well, we just don't yet know.

The End

This heading refers to the end of this book, not to the end of civilization as we know it. We of Waite Group Press hope you've found the information in this book useful and understandable. Note that there are three appendices. The first mentions additional reading matter. The second is a glossary of terms used in this book, and the third is a table of typical EMF readings for a variety of electrical items.

Appendix A
Further Reading

So far, most of the information on EMFs appears in technical and scientific articles. Here we'll describe a few less technical resources.

Paul Brodeur, in a series of articles in *The New Yorker* in 1989 (June 12, June 19, and July 9), explores the controversy about EMFs, suggesting that the utility industry, the electronics industry, the military, and the federal government have striven to keep a lid on the hazards of EMFs. His book *Currents of Death* (Simon and Schuster, 1989) expands on the articles. A December 7, 1992 *New Yorker* article covers in depth the concerns at a California elementary school located near a power line. It also chronicles the problems the EPA had in trying to release the report in which it said that EMFs possibly are linked to increased cancer risks.

Ellen Sugarman's *WARNING: The Electricity Around You May Be Hazardous to Your Health* (Simon and Schuster, 1992) is an investigative reporter's assessment of the situation. The book provides a good history of how our concerns about EMFs have developed. It covers several studies in more detail than this book does, and an appendix summarizes a large number of studies supporting the claim that EMFs are a health hazard. Sugarman also feels that the power utilities and the federal government have attempted to cover up EMF risks, citing, for example, the way the Bush administration delayed and toned down the EPA report on EMFs. The book also discusses EMF litigation and provides the addresses of concerned citizen groups.

EPRI (the Electric Power Research Institute) is a research institute funded by about 700 power utility companies. It performs and sponsors research in areas related to electrical technology. As an industry spokes-entity, the EPRI has tended to minimize the EMF risk, and to cast doubts on research showing risks, such as the Wertheimer-Leeper study. However, its most recent publications seem to grant more credibility to the possibility of risk. At the present EPRI is the major funding agency for EMF research, which some think could make findings biased. The *EPRI Journal* occasionally has articles relating to EMFs. Here are short descriptions of three such articles:

"Exploring the Options for Magnetic Field Management." Taylor Moore. *EPRI Journal* 15, no. 7 (October/November 1990). The article concentrates on engineering aspects such as transmission pole designs, placing lines underground, and the return current problem.

"Sharpening the Focus in EMF Research." Taylor Moore *EPRI Journal* 17, no. 2 (March 1992). The article discusses recent research, including epidemiological studies and the connection between EMFs and melatonin production.

"What Are You Afraid of?" Leslie Lamarre. *EPRI Journal* 17, no. 2 (March 1992). The article discusses risk assessment and communication.

Your local library or utility company may have copies you can look at, or you can write to the following address for more information:

EPRI Journal
Electric Power Research Institute
P.O. Box 10412
Palo Alto, CA 94903

EPRI also published an interesting report entitled *Sourcebook for Utility Communications on EMF* (1992). It's available to you free if you are a member power utility, or for $200 otherwise—a lot for a book that's less than 150 pages long. Its intended readers are utility companies looking for guidance on how to communicate with the public about EMFs. It provides some background on the physics of EMFs and the status of current research, but concentrates on public involvement and risk communication. On the whole, the report takes a conservative stance on the risks of EMFs, emphasizing the uncertainty of current research. It also presents material suitable for public education on EMF matters. Rather than recommend a particular communication policy, the handbook discusses three policy positions representative of those held by various utilities.

Policy A is that there is considerable doubt that EMFs are a health risk. Therefore it is imprudent at this time to spend the rate payers' money on costly steps that may prove of no value.

Policy B recognizes the present uncertainty about EMF risks but recognizes that utilities should take prudent steps to reduce EMF exposure. At this time more costly steps aren't justified.

Policy C recognizes the present uncertainty about EMF risks but acknowledges that if such risks are established, they are of great importance to the community. Therefore the utility should inform the public fully and consult with the public about future decisions.

Policies B and C represent a significant shift in policy, for they respond to the fact that the evidence against an EMF risk is no longer as strong as it once was. In short, the utilities seem unsure of the risk of EMFs, but they clearly perceive the risk of an aggravated and uninformed public.

Technical Reports

GOVERNMENT REPORTS

Office of Technological Assessment. Electric Power Wheeling and Dealing: Technological Considerations for Increasing Competition. Washington, D.C. U.S. Government Printing Office; 1989

U.S. Environmental Protection Agency. Evaluation of Potential Carcinogenicity of Electromagnetic Fields. External review draft. October 1990. EPA/600/6-90/005B

SCIENTIFIC PAPERS

Ahlbom, Anders and Maria Feychting. "Studies of Electromagnetic Fields and Cancer: How Inconsistent?" *Environmental Science and Technology* 1993, 27: 1018-20.

Bawin, S.M. and W.R. Adey. "Sensitivity of Calcium Binding on Cerebral Tissue to Weak Environmental Electric Fields." *Cellular Biology* 73 . 1976, 1,999-2,003

Bawin, S.M. et al. "Influences of Sinusoidal Electric Fields in Excitability in the Rat Hippocampus." *Brain Research*. 1984, 323: 227-237.

Fulton, J. et al. "Electrical Wiring Configurations and Childhood Leukemia in Rhode Island." *American Journal of Epidemiology* 1980; 111: 292-96

Matanoski, G.M. and P. Breysse. "Cancer Incidence in New York Telephone Workers" (Poster). Reported at the 1989 U.S. Department of Contractors' Review Meeting; November 13-16, 1989; Portland, Oregon.

Myers, A. et al. "Overhead Power Lines and Childhood Cancer." In: *International Conference on Electric and Magnetic Fields in Medicine and Biology.* London: The Institution of Electrical Engineers; 1985. pp. 126-130

Peters, J.M. et al. *Exposure to Residential Electric and Magnetic Fields and Risks of Chidhood Leukemia.* Palo Alto, CA: EPRI, November 1991, EPRI EN-7464

Phillips, J.L. and W.D. Winters. "Transferring Binding to Two Human Colon Carcinoma Cell Lines: Characterization and Effect of 60 Hz Electromagnetic Fields." *Cancer Research* 1986; 46:239-244

Phillips, J.L. et al. "*In-vitro* Exposure to Electromagnetic Fields: Changes in Tumor Cell Properties." *International Journal of Radiation Biology.* 1986; 49: 463-469.

Savitz, D.A. et al. "Case-Control Study of Childhood Cancer and Exposure to 60 Hz Magnetic Fields." *American Journal of Epidemiology* 1988. 128: 21-38

Tomenius, L. "50 Hz Electromagnetic Environment and the Incidence of Childhood Tumors in Stockholm Canty." *Bioelectromagnetics* 1986. 7: 349-357

Wertheimer, N. and E. Leeper. "Electrical Wiring Configurations and Childhood Cancer." *American Journal of Epidemiology.* 1979, 109: 273-284.

Appendix B
Glossary

AC Short for alternating current.

alternating current Current that repeatedly flows first in one direction, then the opposite direction, in a regular, periodic fashion. Alternating currents are caused by alternating voltages. U.S. electrical power is based on 60-Hz AC, meaning currents go through 60 full cycles per second of flowing in one direction, weakening to 0, strengthening to flow in the opposite direction, then weakening to 0 again.

amp Short for ampere.

ampere The unit in which electrical current flow is measured, named after the French mathematician and physicist André Marie Ampère.

bioeffect A biological effect.

cofactor A factor whose presence enhances the effect of some other factor. For instance, some drugs, taken together, produce adverse reactions that none of the drugs produce when taken alone.

confounding factor A factor that may make it seem as if two properties are related to each other when they really are independent of each other but are related to the confounding factor. For instance, you might observe that dogs howl more on nights when the spring tides are in and conclude that high spring tides cause howling or, even that dog howling causes high tides. The confounding factor would be the full moon, which is the cause of both phenomena.

corona discharge The discharge of electricity into the surrounding air by an object whose high voltage ionizes the nearby air, making it an electrical conductor.

current Electric charges in motion. A current to the right can be carried by positive charges moving to the right or negative charges moving to the left.

cyclotron frequency The frequency at which a charged particle will circle around in a magnetic field. It depends on the charge of the particle, the mass of the particle, and the strength of the field.

DC Short for direct current.

direct current Current that flows in one direction at a steady flow rate.

distribution line Mid-voltage (5 kV to 35 kV) primary lines and low-voltage (115 V to 240 V) secondary lines that distribute electrical power from substations to homes and businesses.

DNA Deoxyribonucleic acid, is a large, complex molecule that governs cell activity and carries the genetic code. Chromosomes are made of DNA.

dose-response relation A relationship between the exposure to something (the dose) and the effect of the something (the response). Typically, if a particular agent has an effect, such as cigarette smoke increasing the risk of lung cancer, then more of that agent has a bigger effect.

electric charge A fundamental property of nature that is responsible for the electrical properties of matter. There are two kinds of charge, positive and negative. Like charges repel each other, unlike charges attract each other, and an object with equal amounts of positive and negative charge is electrically neutral.

electric field A method of describing and visualizing the effects of an electric charge. The direction of an electric field at a particular point indicates the direction of the electric force that a positive electric charge placed at that location would feel. In a drawing the closeness of field lines indicates the field strength.

electromagnetic field Intermingled electric and magnetic fields.

electromagnetic wave A wave composed of oscillating electric and magnetic fields.

electron One of the fundamental particles of nature. An electron has a negative charge and is the current carrier in metals.

ELF Extremely Low Frequency. ELF radiation consists of electromagnetic waves with frequencies in the 5 Hz to 2,000 Hz range.

EMF Electromagnetic field. Although electromagnetic fields come in enormous varieties, EMF has come to mean electric and magnetic fields oscillating in the ELF range, particularly in the 50-Hz to 60-Hz range characteristic of electrical power systems.

epidemiology The study of epidemic diseases. Epidemiological studies typically use statistical methods to sift through data, looking for possible relationships between a health hazard and a hypothesized cause.

exposure A measure of how much of something is encountered. Exposure to radiation is a product of the intensity of radiation times the duration of contact.

flashover The arcing of electricity from one high-voltage wire to another (the two wires would have different voltages from each other).

gauss A unit of measure for the strength of a magnetic field, named after the German astronomer, mathematician, and physicist Karl Friedrich Gauss.

geomagnetic field The Earth's magnetic field. It is a static field; that is, it doesn't change.

GFI Short for ground-fault interrupter.

ground wire In the modern home wiring system, the wire that serves to connect electrical equipment to ground. Normally the ground wire carries no current.

ground-fault interrupter A device that interrupts current flow if it detects an imbalance between the hot line current and the neutral line current

hot wire In the modern home wiring system, the wire whose voltage oscillates between -120 V and +120 V. It and the neutral wire carry current to and from the power company.

immune system The body's defense against foreign substances, including microorganisms, abnormal cells, and toxic materials.

initiation The first stage in cancer development. This is when an agent, such as ionizing radiation or a carcinogenic chemical, produces a permanent change in a cell's normal DNA.

initiator An agent that causes initiation.

in vitro "In glass," taking place in an artificial environment outside of a living organism.

in vivo "In life," taking place in a living organism.

ionizing radiation Radiation of a high enough frequency to physically destroy or alter a molecule or atom.

magnetic field A method of describing and visualizing the effects of magnetic poles. The direction of a magnetic field at a particular point indicates the direction of the magnetic force that a north magnetic pole placed at that location would feel.

magnetism The ability of certain materials to attract iron.

melatonin A hormone produced in the pineal gland that

helps regulate the sleep-awake cycle and moods. It may play a role in the immune system.

mG Short for milligauss.

milligauss One-thousandth of a gauss.

mitosis The division of a cell into two identical daughter cells.

neutral current The current carried in the neutral wire.

neutral wire In the modern home wiring system, a current-carrying , grounded wire. It and the hot wire carry the current to and from the power company.

neutron An atomic particle having no net charge and normally found in the nucleus of an atom.

nonionizing radiation Radiation whose frequency is too low to physically destroy or alter a molecule or atom.

oscillating field A field that varies in strength and direction in a regular manner.

power frequency fields Magnetic and electric fields produced by our electric power system.

progression The third state of cancer, in which a tumor grows unchecked into malignant cancer.

promoter An agent that instigates the promotion stage of cancer.

promotion The second stage of cancer, in which a promoter triggers an initiated cell (one with an altered genetic pattern) to express its genetic changes in rapid growth.

proton An atomic particle having a positive charge and normally found in the nucleus of an atom.

resonance This occurs when a vibration or other periodic behavior is reinforced by another vibration having the same frequency.

return current Another term for current in the neutral wire.

single-axis meter A magnetic meter with one sensing coil. To get a true reading of field strength, the coil must be aligned with the field.

static electricity The accumulation of excess charge on a body and the associated effects.

static field A field that doesn't change (static in the sense of unchanging).

tesla A unit of measure for the strength of a magnetic field, named after Nikola Tesla, the Croatian-American electrical engineer. One tesla is 10,000 gauss.

three-axis meter A magnetic meter with three sensing coils mounted at right angles to each other. By combining measurements in three directions, the three-axis meter can compute the true strength of the field regardless of the meter orientation.

transmission line A high-voltage line (69 kV to 765 kV) that carries electric power from the power generation station to power substations, where the power will be divided up among the distribution lines.

VLF Very Low Frequency. These frequencies, although low, aren't as low as Extremely Low Frequencies (ELF). Televisions and computer monitors produce VLF radiation as well as ELF radiation.

voltage The amount of electric energy per unit of charge. Voltage is a measure of the electric "pressure" tending to push charges around.

wiring code, wiring configuration A scheme developed in the Wertheimer-Leeper study to estimate EMF dosage by a residence's proximity to power lines. The nature of the power lines (transmission, primary distribution, secondary distribution) are taken into account.

Appendix C
Typical EMF Values

The data in roman font are adapted from Gauger, *Household Appliance Magnetic Field Survey*, IEEE transactions on power apparatus and systems PA-104 (September 1985). The data in *italics* are from the author's measurements and represent a narrow range of samples. Also, the meter that the author used doesn't register below 1 mG.

Note: Many of these measurements strongly depend on position. For instance, the highest readings for the dishwasher occurred just above floor level, while the largest refrigerator readings came from near the rear of the freezer compartment. Readings from electric burners were noticably stronger over the burner than off to the side or front. The strongest microwave readings came from where the fan was housed.

Speaker measurements depend on the kind of speaker, on how loudly they are played, and on the kinds of sound frequencies present in the music.

APPLIANCE	AT 4 INCHES	AT 12 INCHES	AT 36 INCHES
aquarium pump	*80*	*10*	*1*
blender	50 - 220	5- 20	0.3 - 1
can opener	1300 - 4000	30 - 300	0.5 - 7
circular saw	200 - 2100	10 - 200	0.2 - 10
clock radio	*4*	*<1*	*<1*
coffee maker	6 - 30	~1	< 0.1
computer monitor	*50-600*	*3-30*	*<1 - 2*
computer without a monitor	*<1*	*<1*	*<1*

continued on next page

continued from previous page

APPLIANCE	AT 4 INCHES	AT 12 INCHES	AT 36 INCHES
cordless drill	20	<1	<1
dishwasher	40	14	<1
drill	350 - 500	20 - 30	1- 2
electric shaver	14 - 1600	1- 90	<0.1 - 3
electric stove	30	10	1
fluorescent desk lamp	100 - 200	6 - 20	0.2 - 2
fluorescent fixture	40 - 120	2 - 30	<0.1 - 3
hair dryer	3 - 1400	<0.1 - 70	<0.1 - 3
heating pad	4	<1	<1
iron	12 -45	1-3	0.1 - 0.2
microwave oven	600	90	5
radio (AC/DC)	4	<1	<1
receiver	2	<1	<1
refrigerator/freezer	25	9	1
speakers	25	2	<1
television	5 - 100	0.4 - 20	<0.1 - 1.5
toaster	10 - 60	0.6 - 7.0	<0.1
vacuum cleaner	230 - 1300	20 ~ 200	1- 20
VCR	<1	<1	<1

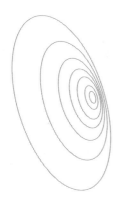

INDEX

Books have a substantial influence on the destruction of the forests of the Earth. For example, it takes 17 trees to produce one ton of paper. A first printing of 30,000 copies of a typical 480 page book consumes 108,000 pounds of paper which will require 918 trees!

Waite Group Press™ is against the clear-cutting of forests and supports reforestation of the Pacific Northwest of the United States and Canada, where most of this paper comes from. As a publisher with several hundred thousand books sold each year, we feel an obligation to give back to the planet. We will therefore support and contribute a percentage of our proceeds to organizations that seek to preserve the forests of planet Earth.